First Edition
Additional Content: Wendi and Jim Dee (www.PureJeevan.com) and
Heather Flournoy (www.katonahgreen.com)
Assistant Editors: Jonathan and Carrie Kraft (www.Strive4Impact.com)
Cover Design and Book Layout: Suzanne Rex (www.srexcreative.com) and
Nicole Byrkit (www.nbcreative.us)

A Better Life Press
P.O. Box 228
Bethel, CT 06801

Gianni, Kevin M.
Smoothie recipes for optimum health: 160+ of the world's healthiest and quickest meals / edited by Kevin Gianni. -- 1st ed.

p. cm.
Includes index.
LCCN 2008900371
ISBN-13: 978-0-9788123-3-1
ISBN-10: 0-9788123-3-6

1. Blenders (Cookery) 2. Smoothies (Beverages)
3. Nutrition. 4. Raw foods. I. Title.

TX840.B5G53 2008 641.5'893
QBI08-600158

PRINTED IN THE USA

www.RenegadeHealth.com and www.UltimateSmoothieRecipes.com

Medical Warning and Disclaimer

The information in this book is not intended as medical advice or to replace a one-on-one relationship with a qualified health care professional. It is intended as a sharing of knowledge and information from the research and experience of Kevin Gianni and the contributing authors. We encourage you to make your own health care decisions based on your research and in partnership with a qualified health care professional.

You may not be familiar with many of the ingredients listed herein. To help, we've included some basic information for many of the more unusual items. However, please note that some of the ingredients are considered medicinal in nature. So, before consuming large quantities of anything you're not familiar with (or, if you have any special medical condition or are taking any prescription medication), please do a bit of research and/or talk to a medical professional when in doubt.

Table of Contents

Introduction

A SMOOTHIE Q & A WITH KEVIN GIANNI

What Inspired the Creation of This Book?

During one of the talks for the first Raw Food Summit, a two-week long online conference on optimal health (www.RawSummitArchives.com), I made a passing reference to a chocolate smoothie I was drinking a lot of at the time. I didn't think much of it until the next day when I checked my email and found that nearly 50 people had asked me for the recipe!

I was a little shocked and a little embarrassed, too. Since it wasn't a recipe made by an expert chef, I was hesitant to put it out to the public. Regardless, I posted to my blog, "Here's the smoothie recipe that I make. Do you have any?"

In just a few days I had 30 to 40 posts and emails from our great readers who wanted more of my smoothie recipes. As I was reading them, I said to myself, "Man, I only have a few." And, the ones I did have didn't really taste very good.

So, I knew that there was an interest in great smoothie recipes and that I could help people by providing more smoothie recipes. I searched around to see if there were any other books that had 100% dairy-free, 100% gluten-free, and 99.9% raw smoothies and I simply couldn't find any. No wonder everyone was itching for new ones!

Now, I'm kind of a curious guy at heart, and I always want to know what other people are up to and what they're doing for their own health. So I thought it would be a great idea to actually ask health and fitness experts what they drink for their smoothies. People like raw food and health experts Victoria Boutenko, Dr. Doug Graham, David Wolfe, Nomi Shannon, Mike Adams, and others. Not many people can pick up the phone and call them and ask, "What kind of smoothie are you drinking?"

So I did just that. I got on the line with dozens of health experts and asked them if they wanted to contribute to this book. As a result, this book you're about to read is not just smoothie recipes. It's smoothie recipes that health experts are using in their daily lifestyle. I think there's something very appealing about that.

Why Use This Book When There Are Hundreds of "Recipe Books" Out There?

Did you know that somewhere around 75% of people are lactose intolerant? I'm quoting Dr. Mark Hyman here.

As the number of people who are interested in a more vegan, more raw food-oriented lifestyle swells, it's important that we have this smoothie book to help people transition and maintain a healthy lifestyle.

The most appealing thing about this book is the fact that I didn't just invent smoothie recipes. I went out and asked the people who are teaching about smoothies, about optimal health, and about raw foods, "What do you actually drink when it comes to smoothies?"

All the recipes herein are 99% to 100% raw. They have no gluten in them. They have no dairy. What we're talking about here are some of the world's healthiest (and tastiest) smoothies. Prior to this book, if you bought a smoothie book off the shelf, nearly every single recipe would contain yogurt. Now, of course, you can still take those regular smoothie books and substitute the yogurt with coconut kefir or something like that, but it won't be the same. You're not going to find goji berries, raw cacao, or other superfoods in any of those other smoothie books.

This is the smoothie book for those who are really interested in being on the cutting edge of great health!

What Are Some of the Health Benefits of These Smoothies?

In addition to being amazingly easy to prepare, smoothies also have enormous health benefits. When making a raw smoothie, you break up the surface area of some of the vegetables and fruits. This helps your body to more easily assimilate some of the nutrients. That's an extreme health benefit.

Smoothies can improve skin tone and energy levels. They can give you a power-packed punch of nutrients that will help any sort of system function better. That's really the power of these concoctions.

Occasionally, someone will raise concerns to me about whether the use of a high-speed blender will reduce the nutritional value of the ingredients. They're concerned that the blender blade's friction and generated heat might negatively affect the nutrients by 'cooking' them or destroying enzymes. Personally, I don't see this as an issue to worry about at all. All of the leading experts listed in this book have had amazing results from these smoothies over many years.

How Can Someone Navigate Through This Book?

This book is divided into three parts: (1) fruit smoothies, (2) green smoothies, and (3) elixirs.

The fruits and the greens are pretty much self explanatory. If you want some energy in the morning or throughout the day, then you're going to go toward the fruit side. If you want to alkalinize your body and you want to ground yourself a little bit more, then you'll gravitate toward the green side.

When we say fruit and greens, we don't mean that the fruit recipes have only fruit and the greens recipes have only greens. We've categorized recipes into the fruits and greens sections when the primary ingredients are fruits- or greens-based. So, there is still some fruit in some of the greens recipes, and there are still greens in some of the fruit recipes.

Some of the recipes in the fruits and greens sections call for powders as well. In most cases, there are many different ingredients in each recipe; so, we have categorized them in terms of what will give you either (1) more energy from the fruit in the recipe, or (2) more grounding from the greens in the recipe.

The elixirs are for people who really want to be superheroes. There's some powerful stuff in these. Many of the elixirs use ingredients like E3Live, cacao powder, and some amazing superfoods. We're not kidding when we say that some of these elixirs are special concoctions—the kinds of things that you would see a wizard making in his tower up in a castle!

You will be able to find many of the ingredients at your grocery store or health food store. If there is something unique, we'll first define it for you, and then give you an option on how to replace it (in case you don't have it or can't get it where you are).

How Are Smoothies a Great Way to Transition into a Healthier Lifestyle?

Victoria Boutenko's *Green for Life* book extensively details a study she did with a group of people to whom she gave green smoothies once a day while they stayed on their regular diet. Many of them showed marked health improvements over a short period of time.

That's pretty telling. I think smoothies are one of the best ways to transition into raw, to transition into vegan, or transition into anything, really. Those words that label a specific type of diet don't really mean anything. You don't need to label what your diet is. Smoothies are just a great way to transition into a healthier lifestyle. And, the habit of making a smoothie is so easy. All you have to do is get all the ingredients, throw them into a Vita-Mix, and blend. I think the most time I've ever spent making a smoothie was probably about five minutes. (That was because I had to peel something; with many of these recipes, you won't need to peel anything!)

So, think about the health benefits and the amount of time you'll save. I think smoothies are the world's healthiest and quickest meals—because they really are meals. They're not a glass of orange juice or something like that; they're full meals. They have fiber. They have all the phytonutrients intact. These smoothies are serious energy-boosting meals for your morning, afternoon, or evening.

Sometimes I'll make a smoothie that I'll start drinking in the morning. I'll put part of it in the fridge, and I'll drink it later for lunch. Half of my day I can go without getting hungry at all. So, smoothies are economical, too!

What Kind of Equipment Do You Recommend?

I like to use a Vita-Mix® blender because I've been through literally six or seven blenders (including a friend's hand-blender that I broke while visiting them in Argentina), and the Vita-Mix is the only one that hasn't broken. It's expensive, but if I had bought a Vita-Mix for my first smoothie, I wouldn't have wasted more than $700 on the others.

When you buy a $100 blender, or a $50 blender (or whatever it is), and you start making smoothies at this frequency, they break. What happens is: Either (1) it's going to start smoking, and you'll have to throw it outside in the snow to keep it from starting on fire (that never happened to me though), or (2) one day you'll blend everything together, pick the thing up, and the glass pitcher will come up but everything else inside will stay because the bottom has unscrewed itself and the seal no longer works. When this happens, your smoothie will drip down the side and coat the entire motor, the kitchen counter and, if you're especially unlucky, it might hit the floor too (that never happened to me either). That's usually when you spend another $100 or so to get a new one. We've had our Vita-Mix for a few years now with no problems. They have a seven year warranty, so, you really can't go wrong with them. The only advice I have is to make sure you keep track of all rubber bands and don't stick anything metal in your Vita-Mix!

Another advantage of owning a quality, high-speed blender is that you'll be able to better blend larger and harder fruits and vegetables, whereas less powerful blenders might not be able to pulverize the ingredients properly (i.e., things like nuts or seeds, or even hard vegetables).

Do Any of These Smoothies Require a Juicer, or Should You Have a Vita-Mix and a Juicer?

Most of these smoothies are just "plug and play," which means you only need a blender. If you don't have a juicer, what you can do for the greens is to blend the main vegetables and strain them through a nut milk bag. With celery, cucumbers, or any sort of greens that you pop into the Vita-Mix, what you should do is wash them with a bit of 3% food-grade hydrogen peroxide, blend it all up, dump that into a nut milk bag, and squeeze out the juice. For the fruits, you don't need a juicer because the blender will do just fine. It's hard to put the fruits through a nut milk bag anyway, because the fruit pectin or fiber tightly holds onto the liquid of the fruit. You're not going to be able to blend an apple or orange and then squeeze as much juice out of them as you will be able to do with the vegetables.

The Vita-Mix is much easier to clean than a juicer, as well. With the Vita-Mix, you blend the smoothie, put the container in the sink, and if you want to scrub it, you can. Most of the time; however, you don't have to scrub because you can just rinse it, put it upside down to dry out, and then you have it ready for the next day. One other blender, popularized by the "Will It Blend?" series on YouTube.com, is the Blendtec®. It looks like it could be a good blender, but I don't have any experience with that one.

You can find more information about the Vita-Mix, plus get a free 30-day trial (and that 7 year warranty I talked about) through this particular link: www.UltimateSmoothieRecipes.com/Vita-Mix. And if you want to try the Blendtec, you can also find it at a discount here: www.UltimateSmoothieRecipes.com/Blendtec.

What About People in Places without Great Access to All These Fresh Fruits and Vegetables?

The best thing to do is be creative. Be resourceful to find what you need. For example, there are different powders you can use that you will find online. We've done our best to provide you with sources for the products, as well as alternatives if you can't find them. While writing this book, I realized that not everyone would have access to some of the ingredients listed. So, I went through the whole book and provided viable options for just about anyone.

There are different cacao and green powders that you can use. I know Superfood Snacks has some great smoothie powders that are a mix of different superfoods. (See www.SuperfoodSnacks.com.) You can also make nut milk. You do this by taking nuts (preferrably soaked and rinsed), popping them into a blender with some water, and then squeezing the blended mixture through a nut milk bag.

Those are probably the best tips for those who don't have access to fresh produce all the time. But, I imagine that if you're out there in the middle of nowhere (for example, in the middle of a desert) and you're reading this book, then you're probably pretty resourceful already and have likely found an oasis of organic produce in your area.

Is This Book the First of a Series of Books?

Let's not get ahead of ourselves here. You haven't even read this one yet! I'd love to hear what you think of this book, so please let me know when you've tried a few of these recipes. If you want to contact me about things you've learned or tried from this book, you can do so by sending an email to **Kevin@RenegadeHealth.com.**

Enjoy!

Kevin Gianni Says...

JUST STARTING WITH SMOOTHIES?

The best way to start is to begin by making simple–or very basic–smoothies. Pick a recipe from the book that has only one or two ingredients. Just make it and enjoy! If you do like it, keep making that smoothie until you're ready for something else. Once you get the hang of making basic smoothies, then you can move on to blending up more complex recipes.

I'd definitely recommend starting with fruits (unless you have a health issue that requires low sugar), then moving on to green smoothies, and finally progressing on to the elixirs for special occasions. This is by no means what you have to do; it's just a recommendation. If you want chocolate and you want it now, head on over to the elixir section. You'll be happy you did!

FRUIT SMOOTHIES

FOR ENERGY, VITALITY, AND STRENGTH

Annet van Dorsser Says...

HOW DO YOU MAKE SMOOTHIES?

General Guidelines

How do you make a healthy vegan smoothie or any recipe you never made before? Ann Wigmore, one of the founders of the modern raw food movement, once said: "Be creative; you only need to know approximately what to do." This is the best way to approach all these smoothie recipes. They are general guidelines, ideas of what to do. Read them, absorb them, enjoy them, and make your own unique smoothies in the kitchen.

Substitutes for Dairy and Sugar

As a general rule, you can make your own variations on all smoothie recipes in regular cookbooks. For yogurt and milk, substitute avocado, coconut oil, cashew nuts, or soaked almonds. For sugar, substitute agave syrup, maple syrup, raw honey, stevia, or medjool dates. Banana, mango, and dried lucuma are also great ingredients for vegan smoothies, as they add thickness and make smoothies sweeter.

A.M. Smoothie (Apricot/Maca)

1 ½ cups tangerine juice
1 whole tangerine, including the pith *(remove most of the seeds)*
3 whole fresh apricots, pitted or 10 dried apricots *(If using dried apricots, soak them in filtered water for 30 minutes before blending.)*
5 apricot kernels
3 dates, pitted *(add more if desired, according to your taste)*
1 ½ tablespoons freshly ground flaxseed
1 ½ tablespoons freshly ground pumpkin seeds
1–2 tablespoons maca powder *(start with 1 tablespoon and add 1 more if desired)*
2 teaspoons flaxseed oil
½ teaspoon edible rose water *(optional)*
Handful ice *(optional)*

Put all ingredients into a blender and blend well. You can replace maca with hemp or rice protein powder. For apricot kernels, either extract them from your own apricot pits or order high-quality, raw, organic seeds online.

Contributed by:

Rhio (www.RawfoodInfo.com)

WHAT IS MACA ROOT?

Maca is a medicinal taproot native to Bolivia and Peru. It is regarded as a highly nutritious, energy-imbuing food, and as a medicine that enhances strength, endurance, libido, and fertility.

WHERE CAN I GET ROSE WATER?

Rose Water can either be purchased at specialty gourmet and health food stores, or it can be made at home. Just fill a pot with clean rose petals, pour boiling water over them and cover with a lid. Allow to stand. Place the cooled mixture in the refrigerator overnight. Strain.

WHAT IS HIMALAYAN SALT?

Himalayan pink salt comes from the mountains of the Himalayas. It is a fossil marine salt from a time before the oceans were heavily polluted. The pink color is from iron content, and it's naturally rich in minerals. A good replacement is Celtic sea salt, or regular sea salt.

WHAT IS ETHERIUM GOLD?

Etherium Gold is the brand name for Harmonic Innerprizes mineral supplement Etherium Gold is a naturally occurring mineral deposit from an ancient sea-bed and contains: Gold, Silver, Iridium, Rhodium, Chromium, and Platinum. The supplement is reported to enhance creativity, improve learning ability, and reduce stress. This is not an essential ingredient so, if you don't have it, don't worry!

Abundant Abandonment

½ cup raw hemp seed butter
  (or almond butter)
2 cups water
Pinch Himalayan pink salt
½ cup goji berries, soaked in water
  for just two minutes
1 teaspoon raw coconut oil
Pinch Etherium Gold
½ cup strawberries
1 teaspoon lemon peel
1 apple, cored
⅓ cup raw agave nectar

Blend all ingredients until smooth. Enjoy this smoothie and experience a natural state of abandonment—a complete letting go of self without worry or fear.

Contributed by:

Shazzie (www.shazzie.com)

Açaí Lime Hot Pepper (Immune Booster)

1 lime, peeled
1 banana
1 original Sambazon™ Açaí Smoothie
    Pack
½ jalapeño
2 cups cold water *(or 1 ½ cups water plus
    1 cup ice)*
1 tablespoon hemp protein
1 tablespoon ground flaxseed
1 tablespoon agave nectar

Blend all ingredients until smooth. This smoothie will help get the blood flowing more quickly, creating a feeling of warmth. Its high level of vitamin A and vitamin C help keep the immune system strong while also supporting red and white blood cell production.

Contributed by:

Brendan Brazier (www.MyVega.com)

WHAT IS AÇAÍ?

Açaí (ah-sigh-ee) is a fruit from the Amazon rainforest. The berries have a rich, berry-coca flavor and are loaded with antioxidants (more than pomegranates, blueberries, and strawberries), healthy Omega fats, protein, and dietary fiber.

The Sambazon Açaí Smoothie pack is frozen and certified organic.

A good replacement for açaí would be pomegranate juice.

Almond Silk Wonder Milk

2 cups almond milk *(see instructions page 19)*
2 bananas
6 strawberries
5 dates, pitted
½ teaspoon vanilla extract

Blend until smooth. Enjoy!

Contributed by:

Valya Boutenko (www.RawFamily.com)

Valya Boutenko, a raw foodist for 15 years, is a certified raw food chef who specializes in desserts. She is the coauthor of the books, *Raw Family, Eating Without Heating*, and *Fresh*. She is also the coproducer of the award winning movie, *Interview with Sergei*.

. . . .

Aloe–Goji–Orange

1 cup aloe vera flesh
¼ cup goji berries
1 orange, peeled

Blend and serve.

Contributed by:

Anthony Anderson (www.RawModel.com)

Kevin Gianni Says...

IS EATING ORGANIC REALLY THAT IMPORTANT?

Simply put—Yes! Take a look at one of my blog posts that explains my thoughts in more detail. Visit www.RenegadeHealth.com/organics.

Also, read this excerpt from Root Stock, volume IX, issue I 2009, by Dan Sullivan. It says a lot about why choosing organic foods is a must:

"Human health care costs are rising meteorically, global warming is threatening our future, lack of safe clean water is spreading globally, and famine-plagued regions will continue to haunt us. When you choose organic, you are doing more than buying the best food. You are investing in answers to four huge problems: Nutrition, Global warming, Famine Prevention, Ecological Sustainability.

Regarding Nutrition: Organic food help protect against childhood maladies, such as obesity and type-II diabetes. Mounting evidence shows that organic produce, for example, has more macro- and micro-nutrients, more cancer-fighting antioxidants and flavonoids, increased levels of beneficial phytochemicals, fewer nitrates and far fewer pesticide residues than its conventional counterparts."

Angelic Cream Cheese

Flesh of 1 avocado
Juice of 1 lemon
5 dates, pitted
1 ½ ounces dulse

Blend all of the ingredients together and serve. This isn't quite a smoothie, but rather a smooth, truly divine creation that tastes just like cream cheese. Enjoy it with fresh celery and carrots, dehydrated flax crackers, or another favorite raw snack.

Contributed by:

Matt Monarch (www.RawSpirit.org)

For the last eight years, Matt Monarch has been a 100% raw food eater. As the owner of The Raw Food World and Living Nutritionals, he is well versed in people's needs and concerns about health. Matt was featured in a raw food TV spot that aired over 15 times on Al Gore's new television network, *Current TV*. This spot can be viewed at Matt's website www.RawSpirit.org.

WHAT IS DULSE?

Dulse is a reddish-purple seaweed. Available in most health food stores as whole leaf or flakes, this raw food is high in iron and is a good source of trace minerals. Dulse also has a high vegetable protein content. It's lower in iodine than kelp, and milder in flavor. Traditional historical uses include balancing minerals and helping the thyroid and endocrine systems. A good substitute for dulse, if seaweed is not your thing, is a pinch of sea salt.

The Anti–Inflammatory

1 cup water
1 banana *(select a very ripe one)*
½ inch-thick slice of pineapple, diced *(including the core)*
1 tablespoon fresh turmeric root, peeled and diced *(or ¼ teaspoon turmeric powder)*
1 tablespoon sweetener of choice *(i.e., raw honey)*
1 tiny pinch cayenne powder *(or a tiny piece of a fresh pepper)*

Blend all ingredients until smooth.

Contributed by:

Craig Sommers (www.RawFoodsBible.com)

Craig was told by his doctor, and also a registered dietitian, that his slow-moving bowels, poor memory, short temper, and other problems he was experiencing were not related to his diet. However, cutting out processed foods, animal products, and eating mostly raw foods caused his symptoms to vanish. Craig is now a naturopathic doctor, author, and raw food consultant.

WHAT IS TURMERIC ROOT?

Many people are familiar with turmeric in its powdered form. The yellow-orange Asian spice is used in curries to color and flavor foods and also as a nutritional supplement. It contains curcumin, an important anti-inflammatory nutrient. Fresh turmeric root can be obtained at Indian markets. It closely resembles its cousin, ginger root, yet is bright orange inside.

Antioxidant–Rich Smoothie

1 banana
2 cups cold water *(or 1 ½ cups water plus 1 cup ice)*
1 cup Stahlbush™ Health Berry Blend *(Marion blackberries, blueberries, black raspberries)*
1 tablespoon hemp protein
1 tablespoon ground flaxseed
1 tablespoon agave nectar
1 tablespoon Vega™ Antioxidant EFA Oil Blend *(or other)*
1 tablespoon ground Salba™ *(white chia seeds)*
2 teaspoons ground Yerba Maté

Blend all ingredients until smooth. The many antioxidants in this smoothie will mop up cell-damaging free-radicals produced by stress.

Contributed by:

Brendan Brazier (www.MyVega.com)

WHAT IS SALBA?

Salba is the name brand of white chia seeds, or Salvia hispanica. White chia seeds (like their similar counterpart, black chia seeds) are easily assimilated and are high in fiber and in the minerals iron, calcium, magnesium, and potassium. They are also a good source of fiber and are rich in Omega-3s and Omega-6s. You can replace white chia with black chia seeds, or if you can't find either, flaxseeds will provide both fiber and Omega-3 oils as well.

WHAT IS YERBA MATÉ?

Yerba Maté is from South America. It is a slightly less potent stimulant than coffee and gentler on the stomach. It tastes something like a strong, dark green tea. Yerba Maté contains potassium, magnesium and manganese. A good replacement is green tea extract or ground green tea leaves.

Apple Coconut Sprout Smoothie

2 apples, cored
1 tablespoon raw coconut oil
2 stalks celery
1 cup sunflower sprouts
2 cups water

Blend all ingredients until warm.

Contributed by:

Brenda Cobb
(www.LivingFoodsInstitute.com)

Brenda Cobb, founder of the Living Foods Institute, healed herself of breast and cervical cancer. Medical doctors praise her for the healing protocol that she developed to help herself and others. Brenda's mission to help "heal the world, one person at a time" is being fulfilled everyday, as the internationally acclaimed Living Foods Institute is now known around the world.

WHAT IS THE DIFFERENCE BETWEEN COCONUT MEAT, COCONUT OIL, AND COCONUT WATER?

Coconut meat is the flesh from inside the rind of a regular coconut.

Coconut water is a natural isotonic beverage. It is best drunk from a fresh young coconut. Look for young coconuts or young Thai coconuts at your local health food store, in the produce section of large supermarkets, and Asian specialty shops.

Coconut oil is a healthy, energizing, saturated fat extracted from the coconut meat. Be sure to buy organic, raw, virgin coconut oil. This process produces oil with the least amount of processing so that the natural vitamin E and antioxidants are retained. To replace coconut oil in raw recipes, try palm oil.

Arthritis–Evaporating Pineapple Shake

½ of a ripe pineapple
Cilantro *(amount to taste)*
1 cup water

Slice down the entire pineapple and throw half of it into the blender. (If it's organic, then use the skin too!) Be sure to include the core of the pineapple, as this part is especially rich in enzymes, such as bromelain, which helps dissolve old protein deposits in the body. Add as much cilantro as you'd like and blend with water. Enjoy!

Contributed by:

Matt Monarch (www.RawSpirit.org)

. . . .

Banana Split

1 banana, frozen and broken into pieces
1 teaspoon lucuma powder
1 cup almond milk *(see instructions page 19)*
2 tablespoons raw cacao powder
1 small piece of vanilla bean
½ cup cherries, pitted *(fresh or frozen)*

Blend all of the ingredients together to make a special treat for special occasions! Garnish with some extra cherries, and some chopped walnuts!

Contributed by:

Annmarie Gianni (www.TheRenegadeHealthShow.com)

Bananas and...Celery, Mango, or Papaya

Ripe bananas
Celery or mangos or papayas
Filtered water
(Amount to taste)

Blend bananas with either celery, mango, or papaya, in any ratio. Add water to achieve desired consistency—Add only a bit of water for a thicker drink, and add more for a thinner smoothie. The smoothie with celery is exceptionally refreshing, especially after exercising on a hot day. There is, of course, no way to go wrong with the banana/mango combination. And, the banana/papaya mixture tastes just like a creamsicle. (You don't need much papaya; put just enough of the flavorful fruit in to change the color of the smoothie.) Have fun experimenting; mix 'n match to create your favorite smoothie!

or...

Bananas and Coconuts

Bananas
Young Thai coconut water
(Amount to taste)

Blend bananas with as much young coconut water as you desire. Use super-ripe bananas for best results.

Contributed by:

Dr. Doug Graham (www.foodnsport.com)

Kevin Gianni Says...

AREN'T ORGANIC FRUITS AND VEGETABLES REALLY EXPENSIVE?

This is a question that I get often. Whether you spend the extra money for organic is about priorities, really. If your goal is to attain the best health possible, then you definitely need to avoid eating pesticides. Since conventional produce is covered with pesticides, then the less of it you eat, the better.

I don't mind paying a premium for organics. Even when we are strapped for cash, it is still our priority to eat organic. That's because I don't trust anything non-organic to be safe. Conventionally grown foods are likely to have had pesticides and herbicides on them. Since pesticides and herbicides kill bugs and living cells, then they will eventually kill me—I'm sure of that!

So do your best, and if you can't buy organic or grow it yourself, then definitely make sure anything you eat with a soft skin (apples, peaches, grapes, most greens, etc.) is organic, as these foods absorb the harmful chemicals much more easily than those with a hard skin.

Berry Blast

2 cups mixed berries
1 whole cucumber
1 large celery stalk
3 cups water
Your choice of sweetener:
¼ teaspoon stevia extract powder
1 tablespoon agave nectar
6 drops of SweetFruit drops
Optional:
1 teaspoon vitamin C powder
1 tablespoon Earth's Balance™ Superfood
   Powder *(to enhance the 'berry interesting' experience)*

Combine ingredients and blend to desired consistency. For sourcing the sweeteners, I like www.cvc4health.com for the stevia extract powder, www.DragonHerbs.com for the SweetFruit drops, and www.Good-CauseWellness.com for agave nectar.

Contributed by:

Mike Adams (www.NaturalNews.com)

Mike is the founder and chief editor of NaturalNews.com, an online news source that covers all areas of personal and planetary wellness–from nutrition to renewable energy. He's written thousands of articles and built a following of over 800,000 people across the globe.

WHEN THE SMOOTHIES CALL FOR WATER, CAN I USE TAP WATER?

Many of the smoothies in this book call for water. In general, I think it's best to strive for using the cleanest water possible. At a minimum, that usually means filtered water, as tap water is often chemically treated and can contain heavy metals.

WHAT ARE SWEETFRUIT™ DROPS?

Guilin SweetFruit extract is the tincture of Luo Han Guo Glucoside (Mogroside), from the Chinese herb/fruit Luo Han Guo (Momordica grosvenori). It is a sweetening product that has virtually no effect on blood sugar levels. It is up to 300 times sweeter than refined sugar and has 5 percent of the calories of sugar. It can be used to sweeten all kinds of drinks and food as a substitute for sugar.

Berry Blueberry

½ cup blueberries, fresh or frozen
¼ cup cashews
3 dates, pitted
1 teaspoon alcohol-free vanilla extract
1 cup water

All ingredients should be placed in blender and blended until smooth.

Contributed by:

Ani Phyo (www.AniPhyo.com)

USING VANILLA BEANS INSTEAD OF VANILLA EXTRACT

For smoothies calling for vanilla extract, you might also consider using fresh vanilla beans, readily available through many online shops (usually for around $1 to $2 per bean, depending on quality and quantity). For a smoothie as described here, try using one whole vanilla bean (a method that works best if you're using a powerful blender such as a Vita-Mix® or Blendtec®).

ARE FROZEN FOODS LESS NUTRITIOUS THAN FRESH FOODS?

Most of the available scientific research suggests similar nutritional values between fresh produce and their frozen counterparts. However, others believe that only those things that naturally survive freezing temperatures (i.e., low water content items such as nuts and seeds) are appropriate for freezing. Some raw foodists point to the fact that most frozen foods are blanched (briefly boiled) prior to the flash freezing process, thus destroying some of the nutritional content. While there is some truth to this, and to the argument that freezing high water content items causes some damage to produce, I believe frozen fruits are generally safe and nutritious, especially when there is no fresh alternative. It's always best, of course, to use fresh when available and in season. But, don't keep yourself from enjoying a great life-giving smoothie just because, for example, strawberries aren't in season right now.

Blood Builder Smoothie

1 banana
1 orange, peeled
1 tablespoon hemp protein
1 tablespoon ground flaxseed
¼ teaspoon cloves
2 tablespoons pumpkin seeds *(soaked seeds are best)*
2 cups cold water *(or 1 ½ cups water plus 1 cup ice)*

Put all ingredients into the blender, blend well, and serve. The vitamin C-rich orange in this iron-rich smoothie will help the body absorb the iron of the pumpkin seeds.

Contributed by:

Brendan Brazier (www.MyVega.com)

Brendan Brazier is one of only a few professional athletes in the world whose diet is 100 percent plant-based. He is a professional Iron Man triathlete, bestselling author of *The Thrive Diet* (Penguin, 2007), and the creator of an award-winning line of whole food nutritional products called Vega™. He is also a two-time Canadian 50km Ultra Marathon Champion.

Calcium Concoction

7–8 Turkish figs
3 tablespoons sesame seeds
Water

Soak the figs overnight in just enough water to cover the fruits. The next day, blend the water, figs, and sesame seeds together. The very high calcium content of the two main ingredients make this an ideal choice for those looking to support their bones, regenerate teeth, or breastfeed.

Contributed by:

Matt Monarch (www.RawSpirit.org)

WHAT IS THE DIFFERENCE BETWEEN A FIG AND A DATE?

First of all, figs and dates are two completely different fruits. Also, figs, which range dramatically in color, grow on Ficus trees while dates, light brown in hue, grow on palms. Figs take on a teardrop shape and contain many small seeds. Their counterpart, dates, are oblong and have one large pit inside them.

Figs aren't just deliciously sweet with a complex texture, but they are a rich source of potassium, calcium, and fiber as well.

Similarly, dates are 'nuggets of nutrition' that supply a substantial amount of both soluble and insoluble fiber and potassium.

Despite their few differences, both fruits are wonderful to use as natural, raw sweeteners–in place of syrups and refined sugars.

Cherry Bomb

1 cup almond milk
1 cup cherries, frozen *(or 1 ½ cups pitted
    fresh cherries)*
1 banana
2 dates, pitted *(or more, if desired)*

Put the ingredients into a blender and blend until smooth. Cherries, besides being delicious, are well-known as a folk remedy for neutralizing uric acid crystals and relieving gout.

Contributed by:

Rhio (www.RawFoodInfo.com)

HOW DO I MAKE ALMOND MILK?

You can make almond milk by soaking 1 cup of almonds for a few hours. When finished soaking, strain them and blend them with 3 cups of filtered water. Strain the resulting mixture through a nut milk bag. You can add sweetener or vanilla for additional flavor. To store, place in the refrigerator in an air-tight container. You can also buy almond milk in a health food store, but it will not be raw.

WHAT IS A NUT MILK BAG?

The nut milk bag is a versatile addition to anyone's kitchen and can be used to make delicious nut milks, as well as different juices. It can also be used as a sprouting bag. There is little hassle or clean-up; just pour the contents of your blender into the bag and squeeze them out into a bowl or pitcher. Nylon mesh bags work the best and can be used time after time.

Cherry Smoothie

2 cups cherries, pitted
5–6 medjool dates, pitted
1 cup cashews
½ cup ice *(optional)*

Blend all the ingredients thoroughly. Chill in refrigerator before serving.

Contributed by:

Dorit (www.SerenitySpaces.org)

. . . .

Chocolate Almond

1 banana
2 dates
2 cups cold coconut water *(or 1 ½ cups coconut water plus 1 cup ice)*
¼ cup almonds, soaked *(or 2 tablespoon raw almond butter)*
1 scoop chocolate Vega™ Whole Food Meal Replacement

Blend everything until smooth. This is a satisfying, antioxidant-rich smoothie that will keep the hunger away for hours. If using dried dates, soak them first. If you don't have Vega, you can use a protein powder like hemp or flax and a little cacao powder.

Contributed by:

Brendan Brazier (www.MyVega.com)

Coconut Eggnog

1 young Thai coconut, meat and water
2 bananas
¼ teaspoon nutmeg powder
4 dates, pitted

Blend until smooth. Enjoy!

Contributed by:

Valya Boutenko (www.RawFamily.com)

. . . .

Coconut Mint

1 cup coconut water
Handful green leaf lettuce
½ cucumber
5–6 sprigs mint
Juice of 1 lime
½ cup coconut meat *(or flesh of 1 avocado)*
1 teaspoon vanilla powder
1 date *(optional)*

Put all the ingredients into a blender and blend well.

Contributed by:

Annmarie Gianni (www.TheRenegadeHealthShow.com)

Cream of Cantaloupe Creation

½ ripe cantaloupe melon
Optional:
Handful ice cubes
Dash lemon or lime juice
Fresh ginger *(amount to taste)*

Blend until smooth. If desired, add water to thin the mixture. Enjoy!

Contributed by:

Matt Monarch (www.RawSpirit.org)

. . . .

Creamy Coconut Berry

1 young Thai coconut, meat and water
1 tablespoon coconut oil
1 tablespoon agave nectar
1 cup strawberries or blueberries *(or another berry of your choice)*

Blend and serve.

Contributed by:

Anthony Anderson (www.RawModel.com)

Dates and Bananas

Dates
Bananas
(amount to taste)
Filtered water

Blend an equal number of dates and bananas in water, adding water until the desired consistency is achieved. Put the dates in first if you want them to totally break up, or put them in last if you want to find bits and pieces of 'candy' at the bottom of your drink.

Contributed by:

Dr. Doug Graham (www.foodnsport.com)

. . . .

Delicious Date–Dulse Dream

1 young Thai coconut, meat and water
5 dates, pitted
1 ounce dulse

Blend all the ingredients and serve. The coconut meat must be thick for this to work out well. When you get the mix just right, it tastes outrageously decadent.

Contributed by:

Matt Monarch (www.RawSpirit.org)

The Digestion Enhancer

½ cup ripe papaya, including 2 seeds if they are ripe *(black)*
1 banana
1 tablespoon shelled hemp seeds
1 teaspoon fresh ginger root, peeled and diced *(or ¼ teaspoon ginger powder)*
¼ teaspoon cinnamon powder
1 cup water

Place all ingredients in a blender and blend until smooth. Fresh ginger may leave fibrous hairs in the smoothie; these may be removed by straining the smoothie through a nut milk bag or cheesecloth.

Contributed by:

Craig Sommers (www.RawFoodsBible.com)

Durian Mania

½ cup durian meat
½ cup young Thai coconut meat
¼ cup dates, pitted
2 cups coconut water
1 teaspoon vanilla extract

Blend all ingredients until smooth and enjoy! Can't find Durian? Use avocado, pineapple and banana together and you will get a similar texture.

Contributed by:

Valya Boutenko (www.RawFamily.com)

WHAT IS DURIAN?

Durian is a pre-historic jungle fruit that grows best in tropical climates like Thailand. It gets its name from its thorny exterior; 'duri' means spike in Malaysian.

A good durian is sweet and has the texture of smooth, rich custard and the flavor hints at banana, mango, pineapple, and vanilla. It's also loaded with minerals and vitamins and is high in protein and 'good' fat. Durian is often called the 'King of Fruits' because of its many physical and emotional health benefits, and cleansing and detoxification capabilities.

Yet, this amazing fruit is not loved by all; people tend to either love durian or hate it— and nothing in between. The pungent smell of this Asian fruit is described as having the odor of liver, dirty socks, onions and cheese. However, the first smell and even taste sensation will change over time; so, enjoy some today!

E3Live™ Melon and Mint Smoothie

1 cup diced cantaloupe
1 cup diced honeydew
1 cup diced seedless watermelon
1 tablespoon lime juice
Agave syrup *(amount to taste)*
10 fresh mint leaves
1–3 teaspoons E3Live
½ cup young Thai coconut water *(optional)*

Put all ingredients into a blender and process until smooth.

Contributed by:

Tamera Campbell (www.e3live.com)

Tamera Campbell is the CEO of E3Live. E3Live (fresh–frozen, liquid AFA) is an all-organic, wild-harvested aqua-botanical, considered by renowned health authorities to be nature's most beneficial super food. Nutritionally, E3Live™ provides 64 easily absorbed vitamins, minerals, and enzymes and has more biologically active chlorophyll than any known food.

Earth and Abundance

¾ cup cranberry juice or grape juice
¾ cup almond milk *(see instructions page 19)*
Seeds of ½ pomegranate
5 strawberries
1 scoop chocolate Vega™

Put all ingredients into a blender and process to make this root chakra (Muladhara) smoothie. The root chakra is red in color and rests at the base of the spine or coccyx. It is connected to earthly pleasures and is in harmony when we feel grounded and safe. Corresponding with the tone of the root chakra, the brilliant red color of this smoothie comes from the cranberry juice, pomegranate seeds and strawberries, but turns a terra cotta shade with the addition of the chocolate Vega.

Contributed by:

Yasmin Gow (www.PracticeBliss.com)

WHAT IS VEGA™?

Vega brand protein powder (www.MyVega.com) is made from whole foods and contains vegan protein, hormone balancing maca, digestive enzymes, and a variety of food based vitamins and minerals. A good replacement is a protein powder and some cacao powder.

WHAT IS A POMEGRANATE?

The pomegranate is a symbol of righteousness, abundance, fortune, and fertility in many traditions. Inside the inedible husk of this beautiful fruit are individual cells containing seed kernels. Each seed is surrounded by a juice-filled sac, which is pressed out during processing. The vibrant red juice is a good source of fiber and antioxidant phytonutrients, which reduce the aging process of the body. Pomegranate juice can be extremely sour or pleasantly tart with a degree of sweetness.

The El Nido

½ cup papaya
1 banana
½ inch-thick slice of pineapple
1 tablespoon key lime juice *(about 1 small lime)*
1 tablespoon virgin coconut oil, liquefied
1 cup water
1 pinch cayenne powder or tiny piece of a fresh pepper *(optional)*

Place all ingredients in a blender and blend until smooth.

Contributed by:

Craig Sommers (www.RawFoodsBible.com)

. . . .

Energizing Smoothie

½ cup Brazil nuts, soaked at least 2 hours
1 cup water
1 large date, pitted
1 banana
1 teaspoon vanilla powder
2 tablespoons raw cacao powder
Ice for thickness

Blend the soaked Brazil nuts with 1 cup fresh water. Strain through a nut milk bag. Then, blend this nut milk with the rest of ingredients and enjoy!

Contributed by

Annmarie Gianni (www.TheRenegadeHealthShow.com)

Five Elements Tao

1 banana
¼ pineapple
1 thin slice fresh ginger
Pinch or two Mandarin orange peel
Pinch sea salt
½ cup water

Put all ingredients into a blender and blend well. Kids love this smoothie, but don't add too much mandarin orange peel or ginger when making it for them.

Contributed by:

Annet van Dorsser (www.RawFoodSuccess.com)

Annet van Dorsser is a busy mother of four, speaker, author, teacher, health coach, and spiritual teacher. She is the founder of the blog, Raw Food Success. Updated daily, this popular raw food blog is a great resource for everyone interested in the raw food diet and natural health.

HOW DO THE FIVE ELEMENTS RELATE TO NUTRITION?

In Chinese Medicine every taste belongs to one of the five elements. If you want to eat a balanced diet, you need all five tastes. These are sweet, sour, pungent, bitter, and salt. In Chinese medicine, you should have all five regularly, preferably in every meal. This optimizes the flow of life energy (Chi) in your body and makes you strong.

This smoothie combines all five tastes, which makes it very subtle, but the basic taste of this smoothie is sweet. This is the natural sweet taste found in whole organic foods, not the pungent sweetness from sugar. According to Chinese dietary therapy, sweet should always be the basis of your meals. Don't let the other tastes dominate. You only add them to give every dish its special character and to get all the different energies in your meals.

Flavonoids for Kids

1 apple, cored
4–8 strawberries
½ teaspoon vitamin C powder
1+ cup water
1 tablespoon bee pollen
1 teaspoon raw honey *(optional)*

First, blend the apple with half of the water. Then, add the remaining ingredients and enough water to achieve the desired consistency. Note: Bee products may be eliminated or replaced with agave nectar.

Contributed by:

Steve Meyerowitz (www.Sproutman.com)

Steve was christened "Sproutman™" in the 1970s. After 20 years of disappointment with orthodox medicine, he became symptom-free of chronic allergies and asthma through his use of diet, juices, and fasting. In 1980, he founded "The Sprout House," a 'no-cooking' school in New York City that teaches the benefits of a living-foods diet.

WHY IS BEE POLLEN GOOD FOR ME?

Bee pollen, the food of the young bee, is almost 40% protein (in the form of over 30 amino acids) and is considered by many to be one of nature's most completely nourishing foods. The alkaline food is packed not only with proteins but with many enzymes, trace minerals and vitamins, including B-complex and folic acid. Bee pollen has been said to increase energy and stamina, increase muscle growth and definition, strengthen the immune system, provide antioxidant activity, enhance sexuality, and smooth wrinkles.

Please note that bee pollen may cause gastrointestinal irritation and allergic reactions. If you're new to pollen, begin with ingesting only a small amount (about ¼ teaspoon) before enjoying this nutritious food in larger doses.

For the Brain

1 cup apple juice
½ cup water
½ banana
½ cup blackberries
½ cup blueberries
1 teaspoon coconut butter
1 scoop berry Vega™ *(or other whole food protein powder)*
1 teaspoon Vega Antioxidant EFA Oil Blend *(or other)*

Blend all of the ingredients together to make a brow chakra (Anja) smoothie.

Contributed by:

Yasmin Gow (www.PracticeBliss.com)

Yasmin began teaching yoga in 2001 and has since trained professional athletes, given workshops in various parts of the world and founded PRACTICE BLISS™. Yasmin is also the creator of the yoga CDs *Yoga with Pilates* (2004) and *Core Strength Power Yoga* (2005), and is the Mind–Body–Soul columnist for *Jet-Set Montreal* and www.Femmeaucube.ca.

. . . .

WHAT IS THE BROW CHAKRA?

Also known as the "third eye chakra," the brow chakra is blue and is situated at the forehead, between the eyes. It is the center for self-realization, intuition and sleep.

This smoothie aides the health of this chakra, as it is pure brain food. Not only do the berries provide a rich source of antioxidants, but so does the Vega™ Oil Blend, which lists pomegranate, green tea, black raspberry, and blueberry seed extracts as ingredients. Moreover, this ultra-virgin, cold pressed oil is abundant in essential fats like Omega-3, 5, 6, and 9, which are crucial for optimum brain and nerve function. The Berry Vega® also adds a nice flavor and protein to the mixture.

The Frothy

¼ fresh pineapple *(or more)*
1 or more kale leaves
Water

Blend until smooth, adding water to blender until desired consistency is achieved. You may want to double the recipe. But, even so, you'll still be hungry for something else fairly soon. This simple smoothie is for the lighter eater, to enjoy when you're at home, or when you have the time, to have before you make your travel smoothie. It is light, but filled with important enzymes.

Contributed by:

Nomi Shannon (www.RawGourmet.com)

. . . .

Georgia Peach

1 peach, pitted
¼ cup cashews
1 cup water

All ingredients should be placed in blender and blended until smooth.

Contributed by:

Ani Phyo (www.AniPhyo.com)

Ginger Pear #1

1 banana
½ pear, cored
2 cups cold water *(or 1 ½ cups water plus 1 cup ice)*
1 tablespoon hemp protein
1 tablespoon ground flaxseed
1 tablespoon fresh ginger

Blend well. This is a refreshingly crisp smoothie, designed as an inflammation reducer. It's not too sweet, although the riper the pear, the sweeter it will be. If you want it even sweeter, add one or two fresh or soaked, dried dates.

Contributed by:

Brendan Brazier (www.MyVega.com)

. . . .

Ginger Pear #2

2 ripe pears, cored
1 cup water
¼ teaspoon cinnamon
¼ teaspoon dried mint *(or 1 tablespoon fresh mint)*
½ teaspoon fresh ginger

Blend all the ingredients until creamy. If you're using a high-speed blender, then you don't have to worry about peeling the ginger. Just wash it and blend!

Contributed by:

Brenda Cobb (www.LivingFoodsInstitute.com)

Gingerly Sweet

1 mango, seeded
Handful your choice of greens
1 lemon, skin removed *(keep a little of the white)*
¼ inch piece fresh ginger, peeled
1 date, pitted
1 cup coconut water

Blend and enjoy. :-)

Contributed by:

Annmarie Gianni (www.TheRenegadeHealthShow.com)

. . . .

Goji Gruel

8 ounces goji berries
3 tablespoons hemp seeds
Water

Soak the goji berries overnight in just enough water to cover the fruits. The next day, blend the water, gojis, and hemp seeds together. This recipe is a low glycemic option, compared to smoothies that use additional sweeteners.

Contributed by:

Matt Monarch (www.RawSpirit.org)

Healthy Hemp Goji Milk

½ cup hemp seeds, rinsed well
1 date, pitted
1 cup goji water

Blend the hemp seeds with goji berry water for about 1 minute, then strain the hemp seeds through a nut milk bag, or if desired, keep in for a thicker smoothie.

Contributed by:

Annmarie Gianni
(www.TheRenegadeHealthShow.com)

. . . .

Healthy Hemp Smoothie

2 bananas
1 cup hemp seed milk
⅓ cup Brazil nuts, soaked
½ cup dried apricots, soaked

Blend everything together until smooth. Almond milk, soy milk, or rice milk can be used instead of hemp milk.

Contributed by:

Angela Stokes (www.RawReform.com)

HOW DO I MAKE GOJI WATER?

To make goji water, soak ¼ cup goji berries in 1 cup water for eight hours, or overnight. Then strain the berries, keeping the water.

You can use the leftover gojis for snacking. The berries can be stored in the refrigerator for 1–2 days.

HOW DO I MAKE HEMP SEED MILK?

Using hemp milk in smoothies is a great, easy way to get protein, iron, and essential fatty acids in your diet. To make it, mix one cup of hemp seed and 3 cups water into a blender. Add honey or agave nectar to sweeten if you like. Strain the mixture through a nut milk bag. Refrigerate to avoid oxidation of the Omega-3 oils. To make almond milk, use the same recipe–just substitute the hemp seeds for the same amount of almonds.

HealthyWay Berry Blaster

3 ounces organic blueberries
3 ounces organic strawberries
3 ounces organic pineapples
3 ounces organic orange juice
2 cups ice

Combine all ingredients and blend on high until smooth–about 20 seconds. Pour into glass, and if desired, garnish with a tablespoon of organic blueberries.

and...

HealthyWay Caribbean Island Smoothie

½ organic banana
3 ounces organic pineapple
3 ounces organic mango
3 ounces organic strawberries
2 cups ice

Combine all ingredients and blend on high until smooth–about 20 seconds. Pour into glass, and if desired, garnish with a tablespoon of organic pineapple.

Contributed by:

Craig Pepin-Donat and Michael Johnigean (www.FitAdvocate.com)

International fitness expert, Craig Pepin-Donat, also known as the "Fit Advocate," and Michael Johnigean, real estate entrepreneur and owner of HealthyWay Cafés, have teamed together to reveal their favorite fruit smoothies. Combined, these two have over 40 years in the fitness and health industries; so, they know what it takes to achieve optimal fitness through diet and exercise.

High Beta

1 ⅓ cups orange or tangerine juice
½ cantaloupe, including seeds
1 cup papaya chunks, frozen
1 banana, frozen

Put orange or tangerine juice into the blender with the cantaloupe and blend well. Strain through a nut milk bag. (You probably don't have to strain if you omit the cantaloupe seeds.) Put the strained mixture back into the blender with the rest of the ingredients and blend well. Variations: Substitute honeydew for cantaloupe, or use mango or any other tropical fruit for the papaya. One cup of this smoothie is off the charts for both vitamin C and beta carotene, and cantaloupe is loaded with the latter. Please note that honeydew does not have the same beta carotene content as cantaloupe; keep this in mind when substituting these ingredients for one another.

Contributed by:

Rhio (www.RawFoodInfo.com)

Rhio is a gourmet raw food chef, author, and investigative reporter in the area of health. She is the author of "*Hooked on Raw*," one of the most popular books in the raw and living foods community. Her extensive website is a valuable resource for raw food enthusiasts worldwide.

ARE PAPAYAS IRRADIATED AND/OR GENETICALLY MODIFIED?

Commenting on this question is tough, as websites with a definitive answer on how to determine the complete answer by examining a papaya's label don't seem to exist. One can, at least, determine if produce is organically grown or genetically modified. To do this, look at the label: If the price lookup (PLU) number is five digits long and begins with the number 9, then the produce is organic. If the PLU begins with an 8, then the item is genetically modified.

Unfortunately, there is no reliable way (save perhaps purchasing your own Geiger counter) to determine whether a food has been previously irradiated. However, organic produce is much less likely to have been irradiated.

Holiday Smoothie

4 cups apple juice
1 cup orange juice
2 very ripe persimmons
1 vanilla bean
2 bananas, frozen
½ teaspoon cinnamon
¼ teaspoon nutmeg
Pinch cardamom powder

Mix all the ingredients in a blender and serve in lieu of alcohol. If you can't find persimmons, replace them with an extra banana.

Contributed by:

Dorit (www.SerenitySpaces.org)

Dorit's love for life and the near-death experience of a severe illness propelled her into writing *"Celebrating Our Raw Nature: A Guide for Transitioning to a Plant–Based, Living Foods Diet."* She also runs a green cuisine catering business and Serenity Foods, a packaged food line that is under the distributorship of Vegan Traders. In 2007, Dorit founded the first Raw Lifestyle Film Festival, which was such a huge success that it is now an annual event.

WHEN ARE PERSIMMONS IN SEASON?

This sweet, slightly tangy fruit, which is loaded with vitamins and phytonutrients, is a winter fruit and will begin to appear in the markets in late September, but November and December are when they're most plentiful. In some areas, availability may even stretch into January. Allow the fruit to fully ripen before consuming; otherwise, their flavor is very bitter. Once ripe, persimmons don't keep well. They should be eaten right away or refrigerated for no more than a day or two. However, you can freeze the unripe fruit for up to six months before setting them out at room temperature to ripen.

Love in the Desert

1 cup aloe vera flesh
2–3 prickly pear cactus fruits
1 tablespoon agave nectar
Water

Blend, adding as much water as you'd like, and serve.

Contributed by:

Anthony Anderson (www.RawModel.com)

. . . .

WHAT IS ALOE VERA?

Aloe vera is a succulent plant whose flesh (the gel-like substance found inside the meaty leaf) has many internal and external healing properties, as well as the ability to nourish the body with minerals, vitamins, enzymes, and glyconutrients. Aloe vera gel is antibacterial, antiviral, and antifungal. It has been quoted as being the most impressive medicinal herb nature has ever created.

You can, of course, grow aloe vera yourself, but you can also find it at most health food stores. A good replacement (though not raw) is bottled aloe vera juice, which you can find at local health food stores as well.

WHAT ARE PRICKLY PEAR CACTUS FRUITS?

Prickly pear fruits are native to North American deserts. The fruits of the prickly pear cactus are rich in slowly absorbed, soluble fibers that help keep blood sugar stable.

Find the fruits in specialty markets; western farmer's markets; and online under the names prickly pears, cactus pears, cactus figs, or 'tunas.' When found in the wild, they're normally still covered with needle-like hairs that can cause considerable discomfort if you're not careful. Do some online research prior to gathering or handling these delicacies. A reasonable replacement for prickly pear cactus fruits is papaya, or perhaps mango.

Make the Sun Shine

½ mango
½ pineapple
1 banana
1 apple
2 tablespoons lucuma powder
1 cup water

This delicious yellow smoothie is like concentrated sunlight. It makes you warm, gives you energy, and lightens up your day. Can one smoothie do all this? Try it and experience the amazing energy of this 'sunshine' smoothie. Put everything in your blender, then blend and enjoy!

Contributed by:

Annet van Dorsser
(www.RawFoodSuccess.org)

WHAT IS LUCUMA POWDER?

The lucuma is a traditional Peruvian fruit, once called the 'Gold of the Inca's.' It tastes like vanilla, maple syrup, and peaches, and is a delightful sweetener. Lucuma is an excellent source of carbohydrates, vitamins, minerals and fiber. It is high in niacin, beta-carotene, iron, zinc, potassium, calcium and magnesium. Traditionally, lucuma powder has been used in ice creams, baby foods, yogurts, candy, and a variety of desserts. It can also be used as a partial flour replacement in cooked and raw pies, cakes, pastries, and food bars.

Lucuma can be found in specialty stores, health food stores, and online in the form of fresh-frozen pulp or dehydrated whole food powder. While there is no equal substitute, try some agave nectar in place of the lucuma if you want to use another sweetener.

Mango Goodness

½ mango
¼ cup almonds
3 dates, pitted
1 cup water

All ingredients should be placed in blender and blended until smooth.

and...

Mango Madness

½ mango
1 kale leaf
1 cup water

All ingredients should be placed in blender and blended until smooth.

Contributed by:

Ani Phyo (www.AniPhyo.com)

ARE 'RAW' ALMONDS ACTUALLY RAW?

That's a tough question and actually the subject of a pending lawsuit in California (as of 2009). It's likely that almonds in health food stores labeled as 'raw' have been pasteurized per a directive by the Almond Board of California. Keep in mind that it's still possible to obtain delicious, unpasteurized almonds from various online sources.

WHAT IS KALE?

Kale is a dark, leafy green that is high in vitamin K and other nutrients. Common varieties found in food stores are Green Leafy, the smoother-leafed Lacinata, and Red Kale. A good substitute for kale is any leafy green vegetable like red leaf lettuce, romaine lettuce, bok choy or collard greens. When eating fresh kale, many people de-stem the leaves. However, in a smoothie, you can simply drop in the entire leaf.

Mango Nectar

2–3 mangos, peeled and seeded
½ papaya, seeded
1 cup coconut water

Remove the flesh from the mango, and cut the papaya into chunks. Then, mix all ingredients in a blender and serve chilled.

Contributed by:

Dorit (www.SerenitySpaces.org)

. . . .

Mango–Avo–Strawberry

1 mango
1 avocado
1 cup strawberries
Water

Blend, adding water until desired consistency is achieved, and serve.

Contributed by:

Anthony Anderson (www.RawModel.com)

Mango–Purslane

1 cup dried mangos, soaked
1 fresh mango, sliced
1 handful purslane
2 cups water

1–2 hours before making the smoothie, rehydrate the dried mangos by soaking them in filtered water. Blend the soaked mangos and all other ingredients thoroughly. Pour into a tall glass and garnish with extra purslane just prior to serving.

Contributed by:

Dorit (www.SerenitySpaces.org)

WHAT IS PURSLANE?

Purslane, indigenous to India, is a succulent, sprawling plant found in meadows and lawns across the U.S. and throughout the world. The plant, which grows from the late spring to fall, has the highest Omega-3 content of any plant. It also contains alpha-tocopherol, iron, vitamin C, beta carotene,

and calcium. Purslane has a

slightly tart, sweet-sour flavor and a chewy texture. Its leaves and soft stems are great for salads. You can steam them or add them to soups, stews, and other veggie dishes. Chopped purslane can also be used as a thickening agent in soups.

In case you can't find purslane for this smoothie, a good replacement is spinach and a touch of flax or hemp oil.

Mellow Yellow for Digestive Ease

¾ cup almond or hemp milk
¾ cup orange juice
2 cups pineapple
1 teaspoon lemon juice
1 tablespoon fresh ginger, grated
1 tablespoon Salba™, or white chia seeds

Blend all ingredients together to make a solar plexus chakra (Manipura) smoothie.

Contributed by:

Yasmin Gow (www.PracticeBliss.com)

WHAT IS THE SOLAR PLEXUS CHAKRA?

The solar plexus chakra is yellow and is located above the navel. Often described as the "center of personal power," it is associated with digestion and self-esteem.

This smoothie aides the health of this chakra, as it contains many tummy-taming ingredients, like fresh ginger. Also, the lemons and pineapples are beneficial in decreasing acidity in the body. Aside from being full of minerals and vitamins, pineapple also has pain-relieving properties. It contains an enzyme called bromelain, which digests food by breaking down protein. Bromelain is also helpful in reducing inflammation and relieves intestinal disorders.

Mulberry–Caramel Decadent Delicacy

8 ounces dried mulberries
3 tablespoons hemp seeds
Water

Soak the mulberries overnight in just enough water to cover the fruits. The next day, blend together the water you used to soak the mulberries, the mulberries themselves, and the hemp seeds. This is one of my all-time favorite meals. It tastes like sweet caramel ecstasy!

and...

The Muscle Builder

7–8 dried Turkish or Calimyrna figs
3 tablespoons hemp seeds
Water

Soak the figs overnight in just enough water to cover the fruits. The next day, blend together the water you used to soak the figs, the figs themselves, and the hemp seeds. Enjoy!

Contributed by:

Matt Monarch (www.RawSpirit.org)

Orange Juice and...Mango or Papaya

Orange Juice
Mango or papaya
(Amount to taste)

Blend freshly squeezed orange juice with either mango or papaya, in any ratio. There is no way to get this recipe wrong; just make it however you prefer...Want your smoothie to be more mango than oj? Then, just add more of the first! This simple, yet delicious, smoothie pleasantly surprises everyone who tries it.

or...

Orange Juice and Tomato

Orange juice
Tomatoes
(Amount to taste)

Blend the orange juice with as many tomatoes as you'd like. This surprisingly good drink is a sure crowd pleaser, especially because the mineral richness of the tomatoes offers an alternative to a super sweet flavor.

Contributed by:

Dr. Doug Graham (www.foodnsport.com)

Dr. Doug Graham is the author of several books on raw food and health, including *The 80/10/10 Diet*, *The New High Energy Diet Recipe Guide*, *Grain Damage*, *Nutrition and Athletic Performance*, and the forthcoming *Prevention and Care of Athletic Injuries*. Recognized as one of the fathers of the modern raw movement, Dr. Graham is the only lecturer to have given keynote presentations at all of the major raw events in the world, from 1997 through 2005.

Dr. Doug Graham Says...

HOW MUCH OF EACH INGREDIENT SHOULD YOU USE IN MY SMOOTHIE RECIPES?

For each of my simply delicious smoothie recipes, quantities are left entirely up to the consumer. Some people prefer just a small drink, while others prefer drinks that are big enough to contain sufficient sustenance to function as a complete meal by itself. Sometimes a thinner consistency is desired; sometimes thick, rich, and sweet most perfectly fits the bill. So, use different amounts of liquid to suit your preferences. Remember, experimenting is fun! And, no matter how exactly they are made, after over 20 years of enjoying each of these recipes, I can personally vouch for their tastiness, and especially for their satisfying nature.

Peanutty

1 ½ cups tangerine juice
1 ½ cups almond milk *(see instructions page 19)*
2 bananas, frozen
2–3 tablespoons Wild Jungle Peanut Butter
2–3 tablespoons carob powder
2 dates, pitted
1–2 teaspoons jalapeño *(optional)*

Blend well and enjoy! Only add the jalapeños if you like your smoothie spicy! If you do include them but aren't used to drinks with a 'kick,' start with less than 1 teaspoon, then add a bit more each time you make the smoothie.

Contributed by:

Rhio (www.RawFoodInfo.com)

WHAT IS WILD JUNGLE PEANUT BUTTER?

Wild Jungle Peanut Butter is made from organic Amazonian jungle peanuts, Brazil nut oil, and Himalayan pink salt. Jungle Peanuts contain 26% protein–higher than any other nut. They are high in oleic acid, contain all eight essential amino acids, and are aflatoxin-free! If you have a source of organic, aflatoxin-free peanuts, you can make your own freshly ground peanut butter to use as a replacement. You can find Wild Jungle Peanut Butter online.

WHAT IS CAROB POWDER?

Carob, native to countries surrounding the Mediterranean, is an incredibly rich, sweet food source that contains plenty of calcium, phosphorus, and potassium. It's also naturally sweet and caffeine-free. Roasted, powdered carob is commonly sold in health food stores. Raw, wild crafted carob powders, while much less common, can be obtained in some stores and also via online retailers. Powdered carob can be used to replace chocolate in any recipe.

Perfect Beauty Smoothie

½ cup red grapes
1 mango
½ pineapple
2 bananas
1 cup mixed berries (strawberries, blueberries, raspberries and red berries)
1–1 ½ cups water

Put everything into your blender and blend until smooth and creamy. Garnish with a slice of lemon. You can make variations on this smoothie by adding different fruits or varying the amounts of each one. Another option is to first juice the grapes, mango, and pineapple. Put this juice into the blender and add the other ingredients. This method will create a thinner smoothie with less fiber. No matter how this smoothie is made, everybody loves it! It is neutral, sweet, and great for children. Also, the intense color means that this smoothie is packed with antioxidants–healthy nutrients that help protect against disease and help keep your mind young and beautiful. Try this Perfect Beauty smoothie today; it will lighten up your day and give you instant energy!

Contributed by:

Annet van Dorsser (www.RawFoodSuccess.com)

Persi–Nana Chia

4–5 tablespoons chia seeds, soaked
1–2 bananas
1–2 persimmons
1 teaspoon maca powder
1 teaspoon cinnamon
Handful goji berries
Handful pumpkin seeds

Soak the chia seeds in filtered water for at least ten minutes. Blend together the bananas and persimmons. Pour the mixture into a bowl. Stir in the chia seeds, maca, cinnamon, goji berries, and pumpkin seeds. For a smoother smoothie, you can also just blend all of the ingredients together at one time!

Contributed by:

Angela Stokes (www.RawReform.com)

WHAT ARE GOJI BERRIES?

Goji Berries, otherwise known as Chinese Wolfberries, are cultivated worldwide. These berries are considered one of the Superfoods and are a very rich source of vitamin C and vitamin A. They are antioxidant-rich and have 18 amino acids and 21 trace minerals. They can be found in dried form in health food stores everywhere. A good substitute for goji berries are any other dark berry like blueberries, raspberries, or pitted cherries.

WHAT ARE PERSIMMONS?

There are two main types of these 'Fruit of the Gods' commercially available: astringent and non-astringent. The astringent type is heart-shaped and contains high levels of soluble tannins. The non-astringent persimmon is squat like a tomato and is far less astringent. They can be eaten when still very firm. For a good substitute for persimmons are apricots, nectarines, or ripe plums.

Pineapple–Mango Mood

1 cup fresh pineapple
1 ripe mango
2 cups sunflower or broccoli sprouts
2 cups water

Put all ingredients in a blender until warm.

Contributed by:

Brenda Cobb (www.LivingFoodsInstitute.com)

HOW DO YOU SPROUT SUNFLOWER SEEDS?

Sprouted sunflower seeds contain a complete array of the necessary amino acids; so, they are a complete protein. They also contain Omega-3 essential fatty acids. To sprout: Soak raw sunflower seeds in a bowl. After eight hours, pour off the soak water and rinse the seeds thoroughly. Fill the bowl again with water and skim out the hulls that are easy to reach. Empty the bowl into a large strainer (colander, veggie spinner, or anything that has small holes works great). Thoroughly drain for about 10 minutes. They are now ready to eat or be stored in the refrigerator. If you refrigerate the seeds for one more day, they will show little sprouts. If you want the color to be fresh, then eat them within about 6 hours— after that they turn slightly brown. To store: Put the very well drained sprouts into a rinsed and dried canning jar (with lid). Refrigerate.

HOW DO YOU SPROUT BROCCOLI SEEDS?

Place organic broccoli seeds in a roomy container, such as a quart (using up to one teaspoon of seeds) or gallon jar (up to three tablespoons of seeds). Soak in warm water for four to six hours, using enough water to keep the seeds covered with water. Cover the jar with a sprouting lid, loose woven fabric, nylon stocking, or mesh and secure down with elastic or a rubber band. Rinse and thoroughly drain two to three times daily until sprouts are of desired length. Sprouting them in indirect sunlight will help them develop green leaves.

Plantains and Water

Plantains
Water
(amount to taste)

Blend fully ripened plantains with lots of water. This smoothie is tough to beat, especially if you like a thick, rich, and sweet shake.

Contributed by:

Dr. Doug Graham (www.foodnsport.com)

. . . .

Pomegranate Berry

1 banana
1 date, pitted
2 cups cold water *(or 1 ½ cups water plus 1 cup ice)*
1 cup pomegranate seeds *(the amount from 1 pomegranate)*
1 scoop berry Vega™ Whole Food Meal Replacement

Blend everything together to make this simple, refreshing, antioxidant-rich smoothie. If you don't have Vega, you can replace it in this recipe with a handful of fresh berries and your favorite protein powder.

Contributed by:

Brendan Brazier (www.MyVega.com)

The Power Punch

¾ cup water
2 tablespoons tahini
1–2 bananas, frozen
Vanilla extract or bean, to taste *(optional)*
Greens to taste *(optional)*

This smoothie is an adaptation of a recipe from my book, *The Raw Gourmet*, called Vanilla Bliss. This is the smoothie to make if you are worried about getting hungry too soon, or if you are working out and feel you need lots of protein, calcium, good fat, and calories. It is a perfect smoothie if you're a growing child, a nursing mom, or worried about being underweight. Each tablespoon of tahini contains approximately 100 calories. So, if you are working out and want lots of calories, protein, and good fat, use double the amount of tahini. If you're not interested in packing in the calories, 1–2 tablespoons of tahini will be fine. Also, experiment with how many bananas you like. This is quite a filling smoothie. (Variations: use carob powder, cocoa powder, raw chocolate nibs, strawberries, raspberries, peaches, cherries, or orange juice instead of water, a date or two for sweetness, or a dash of maple syrup.)

WHAT IS TAHINI?

Tahini is a "butter" made from ground sesame seeds. It is a creamy, oily, and smooth nut butter rich in calcium.

Tahini can be found at health food stores and many grocery stores (often in the Mediterranean aisle). Look for it in a glass jar or a can, or sometimes in a powdered, dehydrated form. You can also find fresh tahini in the refrigerator section in larger, well-stocked grocery stores.

While most commonly tahini is made from roasted sesame seeds, you can usually find it in raw and raw/organic varieties if you look around. It's somewhat pricey this way, but a little goes a long way.

Contributed by:

Nomi Shannon (www.RawGourmet.com)

Pumpkin Seed Shake

2 apples, cored
2 stalks celery
Small bunch of grapes
1 lemon, peeled but including the white pith
Small piece lemon peel *(undyed)*
¼ cup pumpkin seeds, soaked and drained
1 banana

Juice the apples, celery, lemon, and grapes. Put the juices into the blender and blend with pumpkin seeds, small piece of lemon peel, and banana.

Contributed by:

Rhio (www.RawfoodInfo.com)

. . . .

Raisin Sugar–High Heaven

8 ounces raisins
3 tablespoons hemp seeds
Water

Soak the raisins overnight in just enough water to cover the fruits. The next day, blend the water, raisins, and hemp seeds together.

Contributed by:

Matt Monarch (www.RawSpirit.org)

Rapid Transit

1–1 ½ cups water
2 tablespoons oat bran
½ apple, cored
2 tablespoons wheat grass powder
2 tablespoons acidophilus liquid *(or 1
    tablespoon powder)*
2 tablespoons sunflower seeds

Gotta keep things moving! Let's face it: Everything has a schedule, even your insides. If you've ever had to call your plumber because of a clogged pipe, then you know just how much trouble this kind of thing can be. Because nobody likes a cesspool, let's get with the program and have one of these drinks every morning. After all, the best way to get up and go is to get up and GO. So, put everything into a blender, blend well and get moving!

Contributed by:

Steve Meyerowitz (www.Sproutman.com)

WHAT IS ACIDOPHILUS?

Acidophilus is a general name for a group of probiotics that are often added to milk or sold as a capsule. They contain one or more of the following bacteria to aid in digestion:

- Lactobacillus acidophilus(A)
- Lactobacillus casei (C)
- Lactobacillus bulgaricus (L)
- Bifidobacterium species (B)
- Streptococcus thermophilus

Only L. acidophilus is the true acidophilus species, but many producers (mainly in the U.S.) use it as a more generic name for mixtures of bacteria.

WHAT IS WHEAT GRASS POWDER AND HOW DO I GET IT?

Wheat grass powder is made from dehydrated blades of wheat grass. It's commonly available in most health food stores. You can replace it in recipes with any green powder.

Raspberry Shortbread Smoothie

½ pound raspberries
2 bananas
2 tablespoons lucuma powder
¼ cup ground almonds
Water

Blend everything together, adding water until desired consistency is achieved, and enjoy the delicious shortbread flavor of this smoothie, which I adore!

Contributed by:

Angela Stokes (www.RawReform.com)

. . . .

Really Simple and Sweet

2 oranges, peeled
2 bananas, frozen
1 pint blueberries, fresh or frozen

Blend for two minutes or until smooth.

Contributed by:

Sergei Boutenko (www.RawFamily.com)

Romantic Piña Colada

2 bananas
½ pineapple
⅓ cup maple syrup
2 tablespoons coconut oil
1 tablespoon lemon
1 cup water

This exotic piña colada reminds me of watching a tropical island sunset on a warm summer night. It is so gentle, sweet, creamy, relaxing, and filled with warmth. The coconut oil in this smoothie makes it nice and creamy and contains important essential fatty acids. It helps to slow down the absorption of the fruit sugars in the body, which is important to maintain a more even blood sugar and create long lasting energy. It is a great treat for kids, family, and friends. Put all ingredients in your blender, blend and serve in nice glasses. Make yourself comfortable, relax and enjoy!

Contributed by:

Annet van Dorsser
(www.RawFoodSuccess.com)

IS MAPLE SYRUP RAW?

Because maple syrup is made from boiling down the sap from the tree, it is not raw.

WHAT ARE SOME GOOD RAW SWEETENERS TO USE IN MY RECIPES?

If you are making a raw food dish that requires a concentrated sweetener, then use any of the following:

- Ripe, organic fresh fruits.
- Fresh, whole stevia leaves, whole dried stevia leaves, or whole dried stevia powder. Avoid white stevia powder and the stevia liquid drops, as they have been highly processed.
- Dried dates, figs, or prunes. Soak the fruits and then blend them with the water in which they were soaked.
- Raw honey, preferably from a local beekeeper.

Kevin Gianni Says...

WHAT ABOUT FOOD COMBINING?

Many people ask me, "Can I combine proteins, carbohydrates, and fats all together in one smoothie?" This is an important question. I think the answer entirely depends on your digestive system and what it can handle. If it can handle multiple proteins, fats, and sugars all at the same time, then you don't have to worry as much. If you can't, then I'd suggest following a more simple diet.

How can you tell if your digestive system is strained? There are two things that will tip you off. The first is your intuition. It should tell you that there is a problem if any of the following issues crop up (and, this is not an exhaustive list):

- You're not getting enough sleep
- You're getting too much sleep
- Your bowel movements aren't regular
- Your bowel movements are too regular
- You have rashes
- You have reflux

Digestive problems can also be confirmed by scientific tests (which I recommend using). To get accurate results, you'll need to be tested by an M.D., naturopath, or nutrition specialist–all of whom will be able to tell you what you can and cannot 'stomach'. This will ultimately lead you to greater success with food combining and shorten your path to greater health.

Ruby Sunrise

1 medium carrot
1 medium beet
½ grapefruit or 1 orange
1 cup chopped chard, well washed with stems
1 cup water
Optional:
1 teaspoon fresh ginger
10 drops gingko biloba
10 drops ginseng extract
Dash cayenne

Juice the beet and carrot, then put the beet/carrot juice and the other ingredients into the blender and blend on high speed.

Contributed by:

Annmarie Gianni (www.TheRenegadeHealthShow.com)

. . . .

Sergei's Favorite Smoothie

2 oranges, peeled
2 bananas, frozen
1 pint blueberries, fresh or frozen

Blend for two minutes or until smooth, adding water for desired consistency.

Contributed by:

Sergei Boutenko (www.RawFamily.com)

Stinging Nettle Herb Joy

1 ripe mango
1 banana
2 handfuls stinging nettles
Lemon juice *(amount to taste)*
1 cup water

Put all ingredients into a blender and blend until smooth.

Contributed by:

Annet van Dorsser (www.RawFoodSuccess.com)

WHAT ARE STINGING NETTLES?

The stinging nettle (urtica dioica) is a plant whose young, edible leaves are rich in vitamins A, C, D, as well as iron, potassium, manganese, and calcium. They also contain many anti-inflammatory compounds. Don't let their name fool you–lightly cooking, blending, or crushing the leaves disables their stinging hairs. Nettles are available seasonally in farmer's markets, or from friendly farmers' hedgerows. As a replacement, you could also use other edible, wild plants in this recipe. But, be careful with dandelion; don't add too much of it or it will make your smoothie bitter. Enjoy this wild greens smoothie and feel the tremendous life energy it gives.

CAN YOU EAT STINGING NETTLES RAW?

Yes! To pick them, grab the leaves from underneath, fold them like a taco, and swallow them. Eating them this way ensures that they will not sting. And if they do irritate your mouth, the sting will only last a minute or so. (Getting a stinging nettle in your mouth is not nearly as bad as a having a sore throat or chewing a hot pepper.) In a smoothie, however, you don't have to deal with the stinging problem at all...Blending up the nettles rids them of their sting. You can also pick them with gloves or with a plastic bag around your hands to avoid getting stung. Once you get used to it, you can add more stinging nettle!

Strawberry Smoothie

½ cup strawberries
¼ cup almonds, soaked
3 dates, pitted and soaked
1 cup water

Soak the almonds and the dates separately (for at least several hours), then rinse. Put all ingredients into a blender and blend until smooth.

Contributed by:

Ani Phyo (www.AniPhyo.com)

ORGANIC VS. CONVENTIONALLY GROWN PRODUCE

This strawberry smoothie recipe provides a good place to discuss the issue of organic versus conventionally grown produce. The word 'conventional' indicates that commercial pesticides were used while growing. According to a recent study by *Food News*, foods were tested for their pesticide load. Strawberries ranked 6th highest on the produce list, surpassed only by nectarines, celery, bell peppers, apples, and peaches. If eating organic is important to you (as it is to me!), then check out Food News' list of the 'worst' 43 foods to consume, in terms of their pesticide load (visit www.FoodNews.org). You'll definitely want to avoid those that are at the top of the list.

There are many other reasons to buy organic, including (but not limited to):

• Organic food is healthier; it contains higher levels of vitamins and minerals.
• Organic foods are GMO free; there is no genetic modification.
• Organic methods provide for animals; animal welfare is taken very seriously.
• Organic foods are better for the soil; they prevent topsoil erosion and contain more beneficial microbes, earthworms, and insects.
• Organic foods are more flavorful and thus taste better!

For the purpose of each recipe within this book, it should be assumed that organic ingredients are preferable to conventional ones, in terms of health as well as taste.

SunWarrior™ Dreamsicle

1–2 scoops vanilla SunWarrior™ Protein
1 whole orange, peeled
1 tablespoon hemp seed
1 cup water
1 cup ice
1 tablespoon Sunfood Nutrition™
    Tocotrienols
Fresh vanilla bean *(optional)*

Blend everything together at high speed to produce a thick smoothie texture.

Contributed by:

Nick Stern, Brent Hauver, Denley Fowlke

Nick Stern is co-founder of Sun Warrior Protein, the leader in super raw vegan protein. His ultimate goal is to raise consciousness through raw superfoods and cutting edge supplements. You can find out more about Nick and his mission at www.SunWarrior.com.

WHAT IS SUNWARRIOR BRAND PROTEIN?

SunWarrior protein powder is a raw, completely vegan, hypo-allergenic superfood protein that is made from a combination of the sprouted endosperm and the bran from raw sprouted whole grain brown rice. This natural, holistic protein is unique because, unlike most protein powders, it is extracted using a bio-fermentation process. It has a full spectrum of amino acids, and addition, it blends well and is easily assimilated.

You can replace the SunWarrior protein with your favorite protein powder.

Sweet Rejuvenation

1–2 cups water
1 banana
1 tablespoon raw honey
1 tablespoon hemp protein powder
1 tablespoon bee pollen
1 teaspoon vitamin C powder
1 tablespoon lecithin
1 teaspoon royal jelly

Blend the banana and honey in 1 cup of water, and then add the remaining powders. Add additional water and honey—only to achieve the desired consistency and sweetness. This smoothie is definitely rejuvenating for many reasons…Bananas lower blood pressure due to their high potassium content. Hemp protein contains a life-extension growth factor. Bee pollen is an energy food whose rich nutritional stores promote cell rejuvenation. Royal jelly smoothens wrinkles. As we age, our bodies need more antioxidants; so, we should supplement with extra vitamin C. And lastly, lecithin is our best source of the valuable neurotransmitter nutrient phosphatidylcholine.

Contributed by:

Steve Meyerowitz (www.Sproutman.com)

BUYING VITAMIN C

The immune system uses vitamin C for many of its routine functions, and a lack may reduce effectiveness of basic immune chores. Be sure to buy vitamin C as corn-free, alcohol-free, highest purity ascorbic acid; nothing should be added during the manufacturing process.

WHAT IS ROYAL JELLY?

Royal jelly is a rich concentrated food that contains remarkable amounts of proteins, lipids, vitamins, hormones, enzymes, mineral substances, and specific vital factors that act as biocatalysts in cell regeneration processes within the human body. It is a honey bee secretion used in the nutrition of the larvae. If a queen is needed, a larva is chosen and will receive only royal jelly to stimulate growth. Sometimes honey or beeswax is added to the royal jelly to aid in preservation. There is no replacement for royal jelly.

Thai Passion

½ durian, flesh
½ of a vanilla bean
Water of 2 young Thai coconuts *(meat is optional)*

Blend the ingredients of this smoothie, two powerful aphrodisiacs–durian and vanilla–and let this smooth, creamy blend ignite your passion!

Contributed by:

Angela Stokes (www.RawReform.com)

WHAT IS A THAI COCONUT?

Thai coconuts, or young coconuts, are commonly available at many health food stores and generally cost a few dollars each. If in their unaltered state, they're quite a bit larger than what you might expect and are green on the outside. More commonly, the green outer casing is trimmed to facilitate packing and transportation. In this case, you'll want to keep an eye out for a large white fruit, commonly cut to be flat on the bottom, round along the sides, and conical/pointed at the top. A good substitute for Thai coconut water is any coconut water in a tetra pack. Popular brands are O.N.E, VitaCoco, and Harvest Bay, which you can find in a health food store or online. If raw is a priority for you, make sure to read the labels to find out which ones are unpasteurized.

HOW DO I OPEN A YOUNG COCONUT?

Opening coconuts is actually quite simple! The easiest way is to chop a hole in the top with a large knife or cleaver—using considerable caution. If you make several "chops" around the top, it's possible to crack a hole at the top large enough to avoid spilling too much (if any) of the precious water inside. Pour the water out through a strainer. To retrieve the tender flesh, slip a spatula between the husk and the white flesh, and the flesh will easily separate from the husk in large segments. From there, simply remove the flesh, clean it off (cutting off any hard bits of husk that stick to it), and pop it into your blender!

Tomatoes and Mango

Tomatoes
Mangos
(amount to taste)

Blend fresh mango with the tomatoes. The ratio doesn't matter; there is no way to make this drink taste anything but wonderful!

Contributed by:

Dr. Doug Graham (www.foodnsport.com)

. . . .

Tropical Pineapple Papaya Smoothie

1 banana
2 fresh or dried dates, soaked
2 cups cold coconut water *(or 1 ½ cups coconut water plus 1 cup ice)*
½ medium papaya
½ cup pineapple
1 tablespoon hemp protein
1 tablespoon ground flaxseed
1 tablespoon coconut oil

Blend ingredients together to make a smoothie that is great for quick, non-stimulating energy. Since this drink digests more quickly than others, it's great when you're on the go or after you've finished a hard workout.

Contributed by:

Brendan Brazier (www.MyVega.com)

Kevin Gianni Says...

ARE SMOOTHIES GOOD FOR YOU EVEN IF YOU HAVE HEALTH CHALLENGES ?

The answer depends on your health challenge. I'd suggest that you talk directly with your health care practitioner about this—and, if you don't have one, get one! A health practitioner will help you make decisions based both on his or her own experiences and scientific evidence of what exactly is going on in your body. Smoothies can be the ultimate elixir. Likewise, they can be the cause of health issues, such as impaired digestion and candida growth. So, please work with someone who can help you make informed decisions. Guessing about your health is never fun and can lead to neurosis, undiagnosed illness, and poor decisions.

Tropical Tango

½ cup mango
¾ cup papaya
½ cup fresh coconut meat
¾ cup boiled taro* *(or 1 whole red or sweet potato, also boiled)*
3 cups water
Your choice of sweetener:
¼ teaspoon stevia extract powder
1 tablespoon agave nectar
6 drops of SweetFruit™ drops

Combine ingredients and blend to desired consistency, blending extra-long to ensure smooth consistency. This smoothie is high in carbs, but the tropical experience is delightful, and you can work off the carbs by twirling fire batons or playing with a hula hoop. For sourcing the sweeteners, I like www.cvc4health.com for the stevia extract powder, www.DragonHerbs.com for the SweetFruit™ drops, and www.GoodCauseWellness.com for agave nectar.

*Note: The taro plant is inedible if ingested raw because of needle-shaped raphides in the plant cells. Severe gastrointestinal distress can occur unless first processed properly. Boiling the taro should prevent any problems.

Contributed by:

Mike Adams (www.NaturalNews.com)

GREEN SMOOTHIES
FOR HEALTH, HEALING, AND CALMNESS

Abundant Vegetable Smoothie

2 roma tomatoes
1 small carrot
1 small zucchini
1 clove garlic
1 tablespoon onion
2 stalks celery
1 red bell pepper
1 tablespoon fresh parsley
2 cups water

Blend all ingredients together until creamy.

Contributed by:

Brenda Cobb (www.LivingFoodsInstitute.com)

. . . .

Aloe–Ha Smoothie

1 small bunch romaine lettuce
1 thumb-sized piece fresh aloe vera (whole with peel)
1 pint fresh strawberries
1 banana
1 cup water

Blend all ingredients for two minutes, or until smooth.

Contributed by:

Victoria Boutenko (www.RawFamily.com)

Anti–Allergy Super Star

4 fresh stinging nettle leaves
1 handful chickweed
1 teaspoon agave or raw honey
1 kiwi, peeled
1 mango, peeled and pitted *(or 1 cup frozen mango)*
1 ½ cups water

Blend well. Nettles and chickweed are excellent immune boosters and allergy fighters, and the kiwi is the perfect tangy balance for the stinging nettles.

Contributed by:

Annmarie Gianni (www.TheRenegadeHealthShow.com)

. . . .

Antioxidant Supreme

2 cups fresh orange or tangerine juice
1 cup blueberries
1 cup raspberries
1 cup cilantro *(or more, to taste)*
3–4 tablespoons carob powder
5 apricot kernels, soaked or unsoaked *(see page 79)*
1 tablespoon raw honey *(optional)*

Blend all ingredients on high speed until smooth.

Contributed by:

Rhio (www.RawfoodInfo.com)

Artery Scrubber

1–2 cups water
Juice of ½ pineapple
2 tablespoons oat or rice bran
1 tablespoon blue-green algae, spirulina, or chlorella powder
1 tablespoon lecithin granules
1 tablespoon brewer's yeast
½ teaspoon flaxseed oil

Blend the ingredients one at a time, beginning with only half the water. Then, add part or all of the rest of the water as needed to create the desired consistency. This drink will be effective even if you are missing one of the ingredients.

Contributed by:

Steve Meyerowitz (www.Sproutman.com)

WHAT ARE BLUE-GREEN ALGAE, BREWER'S YEAST, AND RICE BRAN?

Blue-green algae, a true bacteria with photosynthetic properties, is the richest source of blood-purifying chlorophyll on the planet and reduces blood pressure. Both Klamath Lake algae (also known as aphanizomenon flos aquae) and spirulina are blue-green algaes. Check out www.KlamathBlueGreen.com for considerable information about blue-green algae and the differences between similar products like chlorella.

Brewer's yeast, as a nutritional supplement, refers to the dried by-product of the beer brewing process. It's similar to nutritional yeast, though more bitter. Brewer's yeast is our best source of vitamin B1 (thiamine), and vitamin B6 (pyridoxine), nutrients that ease congestive heart failure, normalize heart muscle tone, and break up deposits on artery walls.

Rice bran, like other grains such as wheat, oats, barley, etc. have a fiber-rich, heart-healthy outer layer called bran. Rice bran is what is leftover after brown rice is transformed into white rice. Numerous studies have proven the effectiveness of rice bran to increase good cholesterol and lower bad cholesterol.

Kevin Gianni Says...

WHICH BLENDER SHOULD YOU USE?

As I mentioned in the introduction, while you might save a few dollars up front, you'll end up spending more money in the long run if you buy a cheap blender. Sooner than later, you'll have to buy a new one because the motor will burn out. Also, a bottom-of-the-line blender won't blend the ingredients to a smooth consistency. Take it from me; chunky smoothies are just no fun.

There are several great blenders on the market, but personally I like the Vita-Mix®. With that said, I've heard that Blendtec® makes a great blender, too. I'm not really partial to a particular brand; I just happen to have spent my money on the Vita-Mix. I know for a fact that they both can make a killer smoothie, and they're both in the same price range; so, I know you'll be fine using either one.

Vita-Mix, as of the writing of this, will give you a free trial and 7 year warranty. To get that deal, use this link: www.UltimateSmoothieRecipes. com/Vita-Mix. You can also order the Blendtec at a discount through this link: www.UltimateSmoothieRecipes.com/Blendtec.

Avocado Dates

¼ avocado
3 semi–soft dates, pitted
1 cup water
1 tablespoon alcohol-free vanilla extract

Blend all ingredients until smooth.

Contributed by:

Ani Phyo (www.AniPhyo.com)

. . . .

Blue–Green Confection

1 young coconut, meat and water
2 bananas, frozen
½ cup dates, pitted
½ cup apple juice
1–2 tablespoons spirulina
1 teaspoon carob powder

Blend all ingredients until smooth.

Contributed by:

Sergei Boutenko (www.RawFamily.com)

Sergei Boutenko, a raw foodist for 15 years, is the coauthor of the books, *Raw Family*, *Eating Without Heating*, and *Fresh*. Sergei is a raw food chef with numerous culinary certificates who has taught classes all over the world, and he is coproducer of the award winning movie, *Interview with Sergei Boutenko*.

Cabbage Dill Smoothie

2 cups cabbage
2 stalks celery
2 tablespoon lemon juice
1 teaspoon dried dill *(or 1 tablespoon fresh)*
½ teaspoon juniper berries
2 cups water

Blend all ingredients until creamy.

and...

Cauliflower Carrot Smoothie

2 cups cauliflower
1 cup carrots
1 teaspoon dried dill *(or 2 tablespoon2 fresh)*
1 teaspoon dried cilantro *(or 2 tablespoon2 fresh)*
2 stalks celery
1 tablespoon lemon juice
1 cup water

Blend all ingredients until creamy, adding the water gradually until the desired consistency is reached.

Contributed by:

Brenda Cobb (www.LivingFoodsInstitute.com)

Chilled Cherry Caress

Big handful cherries, frozen and pitted
2 bananas
Handful spinach
Water

If you have never tried frozen cherries, you're in for a treat. Be sure to try a few just as they are, before whipping up this delicious drink. They're simply divine. When blending, adding water until desired consistency is achieved.

Contributed by:

Angela Stokes (www.RawReform.com)

. . . .

Chocolate Bliss

3–4 tablespoons raw cacao powder
6 Turkish figs
½ cup raisins
1 small head romaine lettuce
1 small handful spinach
Water

Soak the figs and raisins together in water overnight. The next day, blend all the ingredients, including the water used for soaking, and serve.

Contributed by:

Matt Monarch (www.RawSpirit.org)

What Are Some Tips for Making Smoothies?

Angela Stokes Says...

I like to keep my combinations simple, so that they're easier to digest. I rarely use more than five ingredients in my recipes and I like using water-rich foods. All the recipes I put together are for one person.

Take care to chew your smoothies and swish them around in your mouth before swallowing. Blended, 'pre-digested' foods can be a great help for us in terms of absorption and assimilation; yet, digestion still begins in the mouth. The more you chew your foods, the more effective the digestive process will be.

If you have extra smoothie mix, you can pour it into ice cube/popsicle trays and leave it to freeze for a future snack or add it to a different blend some other time. You can pour the extra smoothie mix onto a Teflex sheet and dehydrate it into smoothie leather. You might find it works better to combine it with something like ground chia or flax seeds first, so that it's less runny.

With any banana-based smoothies, leftovers can also be frozen (stirring a few times during the freezing process to break up ice crystals). It comes out as delicious raw ice cream.

Matt Monarch Says...

Many of my favorite smoothie recipes contain a mixture of dried fruit with hemp seeds. Besides tasting really great, these combinations are simple to make and really great for weight gain and muscle building. If you add dried green powders to these mixes (i.e. spirulina), they become like 'complete foods.' I recommend soaking the dried fruits overnight in just enough water to cover the fruits—not more. After blending up your smoothie, I recommend stirring in a few unsoaked pieces of dried fruit to the mixture, to encourage more chewing.

Cilantro Surprise

1 cup almond milk *(see instructions page 19)*
1 cup coconut water
1 cup papaya
1 cup cilantro
8 large strawberries
4 dates

Put everything until smooth. Dr. Yoshiaki Omura discovered that mercury levels in the urine increased after an individual ate Vietnamese soup, which contains cilantro. Dr. Omura's further research discovered that the herb cilantro could accelerate the excretion of mercury, lead, and aluminum from the body.

Contributed by:

Rhio (www.RawfoodInfo.com)

. . . .

Cilly–Citrus–Avo Smoothie

1 bunch cilantro
1 lime
1 orange
1 avocado
1 tablespoon raw honey or agave nectar

Blend all ingredients until smooth.

Contributed by:

Anthony Anderson (www.RawModel.com)

Daily Dosage

2 apples, cored
1 cucumber
5 apricot kernels *(see inset)*
1 teaspoon Udo's Oil
1 small carrot
1 cup hemp seeds, shelled
1 ½ cups water
Pinch sea salt

Put all ingredients into a high-speed blender and blend until smooth. If there are any leftovers, dehydrate the mix for about 12 hours to make wonderfully soft crackers.

Contributed by:

Shazzie (www.Shazzie.com)

UK author, raw entrepreneur, and chocolatier, Shazzie became a raw foodist for health reasons. Her blog at www.Shazzie.com attracts over 10,000 visitors everyday. Shazzie was so overwhelmed by the positive effects of the raw food diet that she vowed to raise awareness of this natural way of eating to the UK and beyond via her company Rawcreation Ltd, which she founded in June 2000.

WHAT IS UDO'S OIL™?

Udo's Oil Blend is a brand name of an Omega-3, 6, and 9 oil blend developed by Udo Erasmus, author of *Fats that Heal, Fats that Kill*, for people who want one product that gives them all the good fats they need, without any of the bad fats they should avoid. It is a premium-quality product that has a pleasant light nutty flavor and is available in most health food stores in the refrigerated section. You can replace this with flaxseed or hemp seed oil.

WHERE CAN I GET APRICOT KERNELS?

Apricot kernels are significantly rich in amygdalin, or vitamin B17, which may play a role in reversing cancer and other such illnesses. The kernels can be purchased through various online retailers, including www.sunfood.com. Or, you can break open your own apricot pits to have fresher, more potent seeds.

Desert Quencher

1 banana
1 pear
Big handful blueberries
½ bunch parsley
½ head romaine lettuce
Big handful spinach
Water

Blend the fruit and yummy greens together with the water (adding it to the blender until desired consistency is achieved) to make a thirst-quenching smoothie that will keep you balanced—even in the desert.

Contributed by:

Angela Stokes (www.RawReform.com)

Angela went from being 294 pounds to a healthy, happy 140 pounds by adopting a life-giving raw vegan diet. She is currently a raw lifestyle consultant and award-winning author. Her dramatic before/after pictures and raw food books inspire thousands worldwide to improve their health. Check it out at www.RawReform. com. More about Angela can be found in the "Our Awesome Contributors" section of this book.

E3L™ Smoothie

1 cup almond milk *(see instructions page 19)*
2 bananas
1 tablespoon vanilla
1–2 tablespoons E3Live
½ cup non-citrus fruit, frozen *(optional)*

Mix everything in a blender and serve immediately. This smoothie is a energizing and nutritious breakfast! As a substitute for the E3Live, try either 2–6 capsules E3AFA or 1–3 teaspoon E3AFA crystal flakes.

Contributed by:

Rhio (www.RawfoodInfo.com)

WHAT ARE E3LIVE AND E3AFA?

E3Live™ is the only raw, live brand of algae on the market and is processed from the alkaline waters of Upper Klamath Lake. It is shipped frozen as a liquid. When eaten, E3Live helps to restore overall biological balance and to nourish the body at the cellular level.

E3AFA™, from the same company, is the wild, freshwater organic aqua-botanical Aphanizomenon Flos-Aquae. It's available in capsules or crystal-flake form.

If you don't have these products you can replace with spirulina.

E3Live™ Vegetable Smoothie

½ cup tomatoes
¼ cup red bell pepper, chopped
¼ cup cucumber, peeled and chopped
1 ½ teaspoon lemon juice
½ teaspoon scallions, chopped
⅛ teaspoon Celtic sea salt
⅛ teaspoon fresh–ground pepper
1–3 teaspoons E3Live
⅛ teaspoon hot peppers of any kind *(optional)*

Blend all ingredients until smooth.

Contributed by:

Tamera Campbell (www.E3Live.com)

. . . .

Everyone's Favorite Green Schmoody

1 bunch spinach
3 ripe mangos, peeled and sliced
1 cup water

Blend and enjoy!

Contributed by:

Tamera Campbell (www.E3Live.com)

Focus and Concentration

2–4 tablespoons raw tahini
1 tablespoon spirulina, chlorella, or blue-green algae
1 apple, cored
1 tablespoon lecithin granules
1 cup water

Sesame is one of our best sources of omega-6 fatty acids and coenzyme Q10. Algae are some of our best sources of the nucleic acids RNA and DNA as well as DHA, the brain's most important fatty acid. First, blend the tahini (sesame seed paste) with half the water. Use raw tahini whenever possible. Then, add the apple pieces and blend some more, adding only enough water to achieve a whirlpool in the blender. Next, add the other dry ingredients and enough water to achieve a thick shake consistency. Add more water as required to achieve a whirlpool in the blender and a smooth consistency.

Contributed by:

Steve Meyerowitz (www.Sproutman.com)

WHAT IS LECITHIN?

Lecithin is a fat-like substance called a phospholipid. It is produced daily by the liver if the diet is adequate. It is needed by every cell in the body and is a key building block of cell membranes; without it, they would harden. Lecithin protects cells from oxidation and largely comprises the protective sheaths surrounding the brain. Likewise, it is a low-cost supplement that provides choline, inositol, linoleic acid, phosphatidylserine, beneficial fatty acids, and triglycerides. It has proven in human studies to dramatically reduce total cholesterol, triglycerides, and bad cholesterol.

Always buy non-GMO lecithin granules. If you don't have any lecithin, you can omit this from the recipe.

WHAT IS MISO?

Miso is usually made from soybeans fermented with salt and Aspergillus oryzae (koji-kin), a fungus widely used in various Asian food and beverage products (such as vinegars and sake).

If you're looking for a substitute because you'd rather not eat soy, look around for some non-soybean varieties that have become available in recent years. If you have no luck there, you might try adding something similarly pasty (i.e., tahini) and then adding salt or nama shoyu.

WHAT IS THE DIFFERENCE BETWEEN BLACK & WHITE PEPPER?

Different from its black counterpart, white peppercorn ripens fully on the vine before it is picked and has a slightly milder flavor and aroma. It's typically used in light-colored dishes, in which black pepper would stand out too much.

Gimmie a V-8

1 roma tomato
1 kale leaf
1 teaspoon miso (*unpasteurized, any color*)
1 cup water

Blend all ingredients until smooth.

Contributed by:

Ani Phyo (www.AniPhyo.com)

Greek Tzatziki Smoothie

1 cucumber
1 avocado
½ cup fresh dill
1 tablespoon lemon juice
½–1 teaspoon sea salt
Dash white pepper
½–1 cup water

This refreshing, alkalinizing smoothie tastes best if it's smooth with tiny pieces of dill; so, don't blend too long.

Contributed by:

Annet van Dorsser
(www.RawFoodSuccess.com)

Green Chia Champion

8 dried prunes, soaked in 1 pint water
1 tablespoon spirulina powder
⅓ cup chia seeds, soaked for at least 10 minutes

After soaking the prunes, drain off most of the soak-water and use it to soak the chia seeds. Let the chias soak for at least ten minutes. Next, blend the spirulina together with the prunes and the remaining water that wasn't drained (only a small amount). Stir the spirulina/prune mixture into the chia seeds. Yum!

Contributed by:

Angela Stokes (www.RawReform.com)

. . . .

Green Dates

1 cup spinach
3 semi-soft dates, pitted
1 cup water

Blend until smooth.

Contributed by:

Ani Phyo (www.AniPhyo.com)

Ani is the author of internationally acclaimed *Ani's Raw Food Kitchen: Easy, Delectable, Living Food Recipes*, which was awarded "Best Vegetarian Cookbook 2007." Ani is also the host of an award-winning 'uncooking' show on YouTube. Her shows can be viewed on her website, www.AniPhyo.com.

Green Dream

1 ripe kiwi
1 small avocado
¾ cup green tea
¾ cup apple juice
1 teaspoon chlorophyll
1 heaping teaspoon green powder
2 mint leaves
1 teaspoon raw honey or agave nectar

Blend all ingredients together to make a heart chakra (Anahata) smoothie. The heart chakra is green and shines from the center of the chest. It is linked to feelings of love, compassion, forgiveness, and acceptance. For this blend, I suggest chlorophyll, as it contains lots of iron, is alkalinizing, and may help prevent cancer.

Contributed by:

Yasmin Gow (www.PracticeBliss.com)

WHERE DO YOU GET CHLOROPHYLL?

Chlorophyll, the green pigment in plants and algae, is widely available in health food stores in various forms—liquids, tablet supplements, and even powders.

WHAT IS GREEN POWDER?

Green powders are vital living foods that have been said to support blood sugar regulation, detoxification, immune system health, eliminative organs, and much more.

They can include not only a healthy balance of protein, carbohydrates, ingestible fiber, and fat, but grasses, herbs, green vegetables, sea vegetables, algae, enzymes, and probiotics as well.

There are many types of dehydrated green powders on the market, but one of our favorites is Vitamineral Green™, which is distributed by www.HealthForce.com

Yasmin Gow Says...

WHAT ARE CHAKRAS AND HOW DO THEY RELATE TO MY SMOOTHIE RECIPES IN THIS BOOK?

As a yoga practitioner and instructor, I adore smoothies. I often practice in the morning and teach in the evenings. It's not advisable to eat a feast right before either practice or instruction. I usually have a highly nutritious and easily digestible smoothie about an hour prior to a class or practice and then eat a meal afterwards.

Yoga works on several aspects of our being. It strengthens and stretches the body, stimulates our systems, frees our mind from worry and stress, and balances our energy fields. The energy fields we normally refer to in yoga are called chakras; there are seven chakras in the body.

Chakras are powerful energy centers located from the base of the spinal column to the crown of the head. The word "chakra" comes from the Sanskrit word "cakra" meaning wheel or circle. A chakra is often described as a "wheel of light." Each of the chakras has a distinct color and specific functions corresponding to certain organs. When the chakras are in harmony, then the body is in harmony. When the chakras are congested or not functioning optimally, then there is unease and stress in the body.

The smoothies I've contributed to this book are intended to balance and nourish different chakras.

Green Hemp Smoothie

2 tablespoons hemp protein powder or hemp seeds
1 handful spinach
1–2 dates
1 cup strawberries, raspberries, blueberries, and/or other berries of your choice
Handful ice
1 cup coconut water
1 teaspoon vanilla powder

Blend and enjoy!

Contributed by:

Annmarie Gianni (www.TheRenegadeHealthShow.com)

Annmarie is a certified athletic trainer, massage therapist, author, and co-host of The Renegade Health Show, a daily program that "changes the health of the world, one show at a time!" Each Wednesday during the show, you can see Annmarie "cooking" up something in the kitchen.

. . . .

Green Machine

2 kale leaves
1 banana
1 cup water

Blend until smooth.

Contributed by:

Ani Phyo (www.AniPhyo.com)

Green Magic Thunder

⅓ cucumber
1 stalk celery
1 banana
1 apple
1 teaspoon spirulina
1 teaspoon chlorella
½ tablespoon green nori flakes
1 teaspoon lemon juice
1 cup water

Blend all together on high speed to make a smoothie that is full of vitamins, minerals, enzymes, amino acids, essential fatty acids and glyconutrients. This smoothie, which is nourishing and cleansing at the same time, is great if you need creativity and inspiration. For me it's more stimulating than alcohol or coffee. I don't know why, it just is.

Contributed by:

Annet van Dorsser
(www.RawFoodSuccess.com)

WHAT IS NORI?

Nori is the Japanese name for various edible seaweed species of red alga sometimes called laver. Nori 'sheets' are made by a shredding and rack-drying process that resembles paper making. In recipes that call for Nori sheets for making rolls, try substituting romaine lettuce leaves, soaked collard leaves, or Asian cabbage leaves.

WHAT ARE CHLORELLA AND SPIRULINA?

Chlorella is a type of green algae. It is high in protein and highly nutritious (similar to spirulina). For a replacement, try other green powders.

Spirulina is a superfood from blue–green algae. It contains high amounts of protein and is a good source of amino acids and B vitamins. A good replacement is blue-green algae, chlorella, or some chlorophyll extract, which you can find at health food stores.

Green Monster

½ cup celery and kale juice
1 banana
1 tablespoon hemp seed
½ cup water

Because I'm a New York Yankees fan, I might think about changing the name of this drink. I came up with this recipe one morning while doing the dishes after making a green juice. I wondered what would happen if I used the green juice as a base with a little sweet and a little protein. It was good enough to make the book, so this one is definitely a winner. While this smoothie does take a little time to make, it's very easy to put together! All you do is make a celery and kale juice (using either a juicer or a blender and nut milk bag), then put about a ½ cup of it into the blender with the hemp seed and the banana. Add the water to dilute the green juice if you don't like it too strong. You can also use SunWarrior™ Protein instead of hemp, if you want a high quality bio-fermented rice protein. You can find it here: www.MySunWarrior.com.

Contributed by:

Kevin Gianni (www.TheRenegadeHealthShow.com)

Kevin is an internationally known author, a passionate and dedicated natural health and raw foods advocate, a top-notch independent media producer and interviewer, a motivational speaker, and a mission-driven business coach. He is the author of *High Raw: A Simple Approach to Health, Eating and Saving the Planet*, and the creator and coauthor of *The Busy Person's Fitness Solution*. He created www.HealthBookSummaries.com with business partner Mike Adams, and created the widely viewed "Rawkathon" interview series with leading experts in the raw foods movement. Kevin and his wife Annmarie are creators and co-hosts of The Renegade Health Show, a daily video blog that is dedicated to "changing the health of the world, one show at a time."

Green Grasshopper

1 apple
2 oranges, peeled
1 banana
1 stalk celery
1 tablespoon green powder
10 drops stevia
1 cup water

This green powder smoothie is great if you don't have any fresh greens available, if you are travelling, or if you are in a hurry. Just blend everything together and go! Green powder is alkalinizing, cleansing, and nourishing and is good to take regularly, particularly if you think you don't get enough fresh greens. As well, it is full of essential nutrients— you will feel the effect of taking it regularly over time. This green powder grasshopper smoothie is also great for kids (and they love the name).

Contributed by:

Annet van Dorsser
(www.RawFoodSuccess.com)

WHAT IS STEVIA?

Stevia Rebaudiana is an herb in the Chrysanthemum family which grows wild as a small shrub in parts of South America, but it is also cultivated in several other countries. It is completely non-toxic and has been consumed safely for the past twenty years.

The plant gets its sweetness from the leaves, and in its crude form is said to be 10-15 times sweeter than table sugar. The aftertaste is slightly bitter, however. Not only is stevia a good replacement for refined sugar, but it has none of the harmful effects that the latter does—It has virtually zero calories and does not raise blood sugar levels.

If you don't have your own plants growing, you can find stevia extract or powdered stevia in most health food stores. Avoid processed stevia powders that have been whitened with bleach. Natural sweeteners like raw honey are good replacements.

The Green Watermelon

1 cucumber
2 stalks celery
Handful cilantro
3 kale leaves
Small piece garlic, peeled
1 cup watermelon

First, make a juice from all of the ingredients except for the watermelon (refer to juicing instructions in the introduction, page v). Then, blend the juice with the watermelon. Enjoy!

Contributed by:

Annmarie Gianni (www.TheRenegadeHealthShow.com)

. . . .

Hooray for Kale Calcium Boost

3 leaves kale
1 apple, cored
1 date, pitted
2 cups water
1 tablespoon hemp protein
1 tablespoon ground flaxseeds
1 tablespoon tahini

Blend everything to make a smoothie high in calcium.

Contributed by:

Brendan Brazier (www.MyVega.com)

Immune Strengthener

6–10 almonds
5 pecans or walnuts
2 tablespoons wheat grass or barley grass powder
2 tablespoons sesame seeds
1 teaspoon flaxseed oil
1 pinch stevia
1–2 cups water

Blend the sesame seeds in a dry blender until puréed into a meal. Then, add half the water and blend to a smooth paste. Add the wheat grass or barley grass powder along with the stevia. Mix in the flax oil and nuts last (you may choose to use only one kind of nut). Add more water to achieve a thick shake consistency. For best digestion, almonds should be pre-soaked for several hours to soften them. If you like a crunchy chewy drink, add the almonds and pecans at the end, blending only to a chop. Otherwise, blend them thoroughly. Flaxseed oil has anti-inflammatory properties, and almonds and pecans are high in oils as well as copper, an essential mineral for healthy joints.

Contributed by:

Steve Meyerowitz (www.Sproutman.com)

WHAT IS MINER'S LETTUCE?

Miner's Lettuce got it's name from the California Gold Rush miners who ate it to prevent scurvy. It is a common fleshy green leafy plant native to the western mountain and coastal regions of North America. Replace with chickweed or romaine lettuce.

WHAT IS A STRAWBERRY PAPAYA?

Strawberry papayas are basically papayas with reddish-orange to strawberry-pink colored flesh. As papayas go, the strawberry-flesh papayas are known as especially sweet and delicious. If you can't find strawberry papayas, substitute with normal papayas.

Key of "C"

2 cups miner's lettuce
1 ripe strawberry papaya, peeled and
    sliced
1 banana
1 cup apple juice

Blend all ingredients for two minutes or until smooth.

Contributed by:

Victoria Boutenko
(www.RawFamily.com)

Victoria Boutenko lives in Ashland, Oregon. She is the award-winning author of *Green For Life*, *Raw Family*, *12 Steps to Raw Foods*, and several raw recipe books. She teaches classes on raw food all over the world. As a result of her teachings, many raw food communities have formed in numerous countries. She continues traveling worldwide, sharing her gourmet raw cuisine and her inspiring story of change, faith, and determination.

Malted Greens

1 cup almond milk *(see instructions page 19)*
1–2 cups red chard leaves
1 banana
6 large strawberries
4 dates, pitted
1 tablespoon carob powder

When preparing the red chard, cut out the stems and save for another use. Start with 1 cup leaves, adding more according to your own taste. Put all ingredients into a blender and blend until smooth. If this doesn't taste like a malt, then I'm hallucinating…but in a good way!

Contributed by:

Rhio (www.RawFoodInfo.com)

WHAT IS RED CHARD?

Red chard is a member of the Swiss chard family. The red refers to the color of the stem. Chard has a mild, slightly sweet flavor, and is excellent for juicing and for light cooking. Like spinach, uncooked chard contains oxalic acid, which binds with calcium and can diminish the absorption of calcium in our bodies. Red chard can be replaced with any chard, beet greens, or spinach.

Mega Vega™ Green Smoothie

½ cup apple juice
½ cup almond or rice milk
1 scoop Natural Vega *(or other protein powder)*
1 banana
½ apple
Handful sunflower sprouts
1 teaspoon tahini

For the Mega Vega Green Smoothie, I add sunflower sprouts for crunch and at least one scoop of natural flavor Vega for the chlorella protein.

Contributed by:

Brendan Brazier (www.MyVega.com)

. . . .

Merry Mushroom–Mango Monsoon

1 handful spinach
2 mangos, peeled and seeded
1 dropper marine phytoplankton
1 tablespoon ground flaxseed
1 teaspoon cordiceps
Water

Blend all ingredients, adding water until desired consistency is achieved. Enjoy!

Contributed by:

Kevin Gianni (www.TheRenegadeHealthShow.com)

Molten Ecstatic Beings

½ cup pumpkin seeds, soaked for at least two hours
2 cups water
Pinch Himalayan pink salt
½ cup goji berries, soaked for just two minutes
⅓ cup agave nectar
¼ teaspoon ho shou wu *(also known as fo-ti)*
5 young dandelion leaves

Inside every couch potato there's an ecstatic being trying to get out. Blend everything together until smooth make a smoothie that'll make everyone shine.

Contributed by:

Rhio (www.RawfoodInfo.com)

WHAT IS HO SHOU WU?

Ho Shou Wu, or Fo-Ti, is a much honored herb that has been known in Asia for centuries for it's longevity and beneficial rejuvenating effects. Highly prized in China as an adaptogenic herb, Ho Shou Wu possesses properties similar to ginseng and increases strength in the liver, kidneys, bones, and muscles. It is known to calm the nervous system and clear the eyes. A member of the buckwheat family, ho shou wu contains bioflavonoid-like compounds that help protect and maintain blood vessel health. You can find this remarkable herb in health food stores everywhere.

Nomi's Favorite Green Smoothie

1 cup juice from 2–3 oranges or tangerines
5–6 cups assorted greens *(start with 2-3 cups)*
1 cup papaya *(for smooth consistency)*
Any supplements you care to take
1–3 bananas, frozen

Blend to a smooth consistency as rapidly as possible to keep it cold. You might want to start out with fewer greens, because it might take awhile before you begin to crave that slight bitter taste that tons of greens will give to a smoothie.

Contributed by:

Nomi Shannon (www.RawGourmet.com)

. . . .

One Hot Tomato

1 red bell pepper
1 cup very ripe tomato
1 stalk celery
½ teaspoon dried oregano
1 tablespoon flaxseed oil
Pinch cayenne pepper
1 ½ cups water

Blend all ingredients until warm.

Contributed by:

Brenda Cobb (www.LivingFoodsInstitute.com)

Nomi Shannon Says...

WHAT SHOULD YOU EAT?

Over the years, wherever I go, the one question I hear the most is: "But what should I eat?" Whether you'd simply like to add more fruit and vegetable servings to your diet, or want to change your lifestyle in a more dramatic way, this book is an to answer that question. It includes recipes for all occasions, most of them very simple, so that you will be able to enjoy a variety of food with no more expenditure of time than in a traditional Standard American Diet (SAD) kitchen.

Although you may find this hard to believe right now, once you get into the rhythm of raw food preparation, you will likely spend less time in your kitchen than you did before. You will see that a raw food diet can be as exciting and interesting as any other type of cuisine. The recipes will give you the tools to prepare meals for all occasions that are tasty, nutritious, and easy to make.

The challenge is in becoming educated and receiving the support you need while making this change in the way you prepare and eat your food. You need to become aware of the sources available to you, where to get the supplies, and how to use them. Look for ways to obtain the equipment, food, and guidance you need, no matter where you live.

One Man Went to Mow, Went to Mow a Meadow

Juice of one lemon
Juice of one orange
1 teaspoon lemon rind, grated
1 pear, cored
⅓ cup dried barley grass
3 ½ ounces (100g) shelled hemp seeds
2 teaspoons raw tahini
2 teaspoons raw agave nectar

In this green and pleasant land, all I can do is love what Gaia has gifted me with. Green. A world away from Greed. Add all ingredients to a high-speed blender and blend until smooth.

Contributed by:

Shazzie (www.shazzie.com)

WHAT IS DRIED BARLEY GRASS?

The "grass" of barley grass is really the leaves of the barley plant. Dried barley grass is an all-around highly nutritious food and said to have 30 times more vitamin B1 and 11 times the amount of calcium than there is in cow's milk, 6.5 times as much carotene and nearly 5 times the iron content of spinach, close to seven times the vitamin C in oranges, four times the vitamin B1 in whole wheat flour, and 80 micrograms of vitamin B12 per 100 grams of dried barley plant juice. It also contains one of the most amazing nutrients, chlorophyll (liquid oxygenated sunshine), a natural detoxifier that rids the intestines of stored toxins. What's more, barley grass is believed to contain up to 1,000 enzymes, the necessary regulators of the body.

For a substitute for barley grass powder, try wheat grass powder.

Plum–Apple–Kale Smoothie

4 plums *(1 cup)*
1 apple
½ bunch kale *(or more, amount to taste)*

Blend all ingredients until smooth. Kale is a cruciferous vegetable that has been shown to have anti-cancer properties.

Contributed by:

Nomi Shannon (www.RawGourmet.com)

Nomi Shannon was introduced to raw food in 1987 by her holistic physician and since then she has said "good riddance" to fibromyalgia, hypoglycemia, digestive disorders, and a host of other maladies. She soon began working as a health consultant at the world-renowned Hippocrates Health Institute in Florida. Nomi is now an author, raw food consultant, and gourmet chef.

Simplicity's Kiss

3 bananas
1 head romaine lettuce
Water

Chop ingredients, if necessary, then blend everything, adding water until desired consistency is achieved. This is a green smoothie stripped down to its bare bones. Despite the 'über-short' ingredient list, this is truly one of my favorite smoothie blends—it is so simple, clean-feeling, and delightful. I also like to swirl whole goji berries into this smoothie to encourage myself to chew and drink it more slowly. Otherwise, it is so easy to guzzle this green kiss of simpl-
icity straight down.

and...

Spicy Carrot Smoothie

2 cups carrots
1 cup celery
1 tablespoon garlic
Pinch cayenne pepper
¼ teaspoon cinnamon
2 cups water

Blend all of the ingredients until creamy.

Contributed by:

Angela Stokes (www.RawReform.com)

Spicy Green Smoothie

2 cups kale
1 apple
1 stalk celery
1 clove garlic
1 tablespoon lemon juice
1 tablespoon fresh ginger
2 cups water

Blend all the ingredients until creamy. Add the water gradually until desired consistency is reached.

Contributed by:

Brenda Cobb (www.LivingFoodsInstitute.com)

. . . .

Squash–Parsley

2 large coconuts, meat and water
1 bunch parsley
½ cup squash, chopped
¼ teaspoon lemon juice
Pinch cinnamon

Blend thoroughly. Chill before serving, if desired, or serve as is.

Contributed by:

Dorit (www.SerenitySpaces.org)

Strawberry–Kiwi

1 cup strawberries
2 bananas, frozen
1 kiwi
½ bunch romaine lettuce
2 cups coconut water

Remove the stems from the strawberries if desired, and blend all ingredients to desired consistency. This makes a very delicious liquid breakfast or lunch.

and...

Strawphistilantro

1 bunch cilantro
1 pound strawberries
2 bananas
Water

Remove the stems from the strawberries if desired, and blend all ingredients togehter, adding water until desired consistency is achieved. This makes a very delicious liquid breakfast or lunch.

Contributed by:

Dorit (www.SerenitySpaces.org)

Summer Cuke Cooler

1 large cucumber
¼ cup goji berries
1 grapefruit
Honey or agave nectar *(amount to taste)*
Water

Blend all ingredients, adding water until desired consistency is achieved.

and...

Sunny Berries

Big handful sunflower greens
½ pound fresh raspberries
2 apples
Water

I love, love, LOVE sunflower greens. This gentle, sweet blend of them feels so fresh and delicate. Blend, adding water until desired consistency is achieved.

Contributed by:

Nomi Shannon (www.RawGourmet.com)

WHAT ARE SUNFLOWER GREENS?

Sunflower greens are baby greens grown from sunflower seeds and are known for having a crisp nutty flavor. The nutritional powerhouses are rich in nutrients, including vitamins A, B, C, and E, and zinc, chlorophyll, iron, magnesium, niacin, phosphorus, potassium, amino acids, and protein.

As well, sunflower seeds are easily grown at home. For the highest nutrient value, growing them in soil and in natural sunlight is the best. A spot near a sunny kitchen window works best.

For a replacement, try various other baby greens.

Sweet and Sour Smoothie

2 cups apple juice, freshly made
3 Bosc pears
1 cup raspberries
4–5 kale leaves
1 teaspoon lemon juice

Make the apple juice first, then pour it and the other ingredients into the blender. Mix to desired consistency, then serve chilled or as–is. The Bosc pears, firmer and denser than other pears, can be replaced with any other variety.

Contributed by:

Dorit (www.SerenitySpaces.org)

. . . .

Sweet Green

6 leaves romaine lettuce
2 dates, pitted
½ melon *(any kind)*
2 cups water
1 tablespoon ground flaxseed
1 tablespoon hemp protein
½ tablespoon fresh ginger, grated

Blend all the ingredients together to make a surprisingly sweet, fresh smoothie.

Contributed by:

Brendan Brazier (www.MyVega.com)

Brendan Brazier Says...

HOW CAN YOU CAN VARY INGREDIENTS?

I usually peel and freeze bananas ahead of time so that I have a handy supply at all times. Adding them frozen to smoothies is like adding a form of ice, and it helps blend all the ingredients together for a smooth, thick consistency. You can also substitute ice cubes for some of the water. Using frozen fruit and ice cubes makes the smoothies thicker, which has even been shown to ward off hunger even longer.

To significantly increase nutrient value, substitute hemp and ground flax in any of the recipes for Vega™ Whole Food Smoothie Infusion on a 1:1 ratio. For the ultimate in nutrient density, substitute for Vega Whole Food Meal Replacement.

Following are sources I recommend for getting some of my favorite smoothie ingredients:

Frozen fruit: Stahlbush Island Farms (www.Stahlbush.com)
Coconut water: O.N.E. (www.OneNaturalExperience.com)
Açaí: Sambazon (www.Sambazon.com)
Yerba Maté: Guayaki (www.Guayaki.com)
Hemp: Manitoba Harvest (www.ManitobaHarvest.com)
Salba: (www.Salbaus.com)
Vega: (www.MyVega.com)

WHAT IS CHICKWEED?

Chickweed is a common edible and medicinal plant that grows wild throughout North America. It's best eaten raw in early spring or late fall. The tea, tincture, or encapsulated herb made from chickweed is a mild diuretic and soothes the kidneys and urinary tract and helps relieve cystitis. Chickweed is an excellent source of vitamins A, D, B complex, C, and rutin, and trace minerals.

Chickweed can be replaced with any leafy green lettuce.

Very Wild & Edible

2 cups chickweed
½ cup fresh mint
2–3 ripe pears
½ avocado
½ cup apple juice
1 cup water

Blend all ingredients until smooth.

and...

Victoria's Favorite

1 bunch fresh dandelions
1 cup pineapple, cubed
1 mango, peeled and sliced
1 cup water

Blend to all ingredients for two minutes, or until smooth.

Contributed by:

Victoria Boutenko
(www.RawFamily.com)

Wonderfully Smooth Peach–Spinach

6 peaches, pitted
4 handfuls spinach
2 cups coconut water

Blend to desired texture.

Contributed by:

Dorit (www.SerenitySpaces.org)

. . . .

Zucchini Herb Smoothie

2 cups zucchini
1 clove garlic
1 tablespoon lemon juice
½ teaspoon dried basil
½ teaspoon dried thyme
¼ teaspoon dried dill
2 cups water

Blend all ingredients until creamy. Note: You may substitute any of the dried herbs with 1 tablespoon of fresh herbs.

Contributed by:

Brenda Cobb (www.LivingFoodsInstitute.com)

ELIXIR RECIPES

FOR DETOX, CLARITY, AND SUPERHUMAN POWERS

Kevin Gianni Says...

ARE SUPPLEMENTS NEEDED IF YOU'RE DRINKING SMOOTHIES EVERYDAY?

The best answer I can give you is: It's debatable. So, what I recommend is to see a naturopath, a chiropractor, or someone who's trained in physiological testing—whether it's applied kinesiology, or saliva testing, or blood testing. A good health care professional can find out what sort of things might be going on in your body. Using a test as a baseline, you can then start a health regimen. Go back to your practitioner in one to two months for a follow up and see if the protocol you've been following is working. I believe that is really one of the best ways to regulate your progress or health.

We can get so caught up eating smoothies (or anything else) and think that we're getting the best nutrition in the world. However, if our digestive system isn't functioning properly, all those nutrients just go out the other end—without being assimilated into the body. You can get sick or tired (or sick and tired), or you could get a rash on your stomach (or any other number of things), and you may think you're eating healthfully but wonder why you aren't experiencing optimal health. Maybe it's because your digestive system (or your kidneys, your liver, etc.) isn't working properly. Or, perhaps you're not flushing out toxins and acidity from the body. Or, maybe it's something else. The nice thing is that with the tests available today, we don't have to guess with these things anymore.

So, I truly recommend physiological testing. If you are interested in whether or not taking supplements is necessary, or if you should just drink smoothies, or if you should eat a raw diet, or if you should eat a vegan diet (etc., etc., etc.), then consult a health care practitioner. Get a baseline test and find out how good your health truly is and how to improve it. That keep you from guessing all the time about whether or not something is working.

Alert and Creative

1–2 cups water
2–4 tablespoons sunflower seeds
1 apple, cored
1 tablespoon chlorella, spirulina, or blue-green algae
1 teaspoon flaxseed, hemp, or evening primrose oil
1 tablespoon lecithin granules
Pinch stevia *(optional)*

Start by blending 1 cup of water and the sunflower seeds until smooth. Add the apple piece by piece and blend. Add the remaining ingredients and only enough water to achieve a thick shake consistency. If you like a nutty, chewy drink, add the sunflowers at the end and only blend for a few seconds. The neuropeptides in algae are small enough to pass through the blood-brain barrier, giving a quick boost to levels of alertness and concentration. Flax, hemp, and evening primrose oils are superb sources of Omega-3 essential fatty acids and particularly Alpha-linolenic acid (LNA), which is the precursor for DHA, the most abundant fat in the brain. Lecithin is our best source of phospholipids, which stimulate intelligence. Stevia is a non-sugar sweetener.

Contributed by:

Steve Meyerowitz (www.Sproutman.com)

WHAT IS THE THROAT CHAKRA?

The throat chakra is blue and is located at the throat. It is associated with communication, truth, trust, and the thyroid gland. The blueberries in this smoothie aide the health of this chakra, as they are packed with antioxidants, which help regenerate the capillaries and vascular system. E3Live™ also supports this chakra; it is abundant in nutrient-dense chlorophyll and minerals that support the thyroid gland and speed up cell rejuvenation.

WHAT IS BLACK SESAME TAHINI?

Tahini is a 'butter' made from ground sesame seeds. Black sesame tahini is essentially the same as the more commonly found brownish variety, only it's made using black sesame seeds. It may be tough to locate this product at your local health food store, but it's readily available online.

Berry Blue

¾ cup soy milk
¾ cup pineapple juice
½ cup blueberries
6–8 purple grapes
1 teaspoon E3Live™

Blend to desired consistency to make a throat chakra (Visuddha) smoothie. If you want 100% raw, replace soy milk with almond or hemp milk. If you don't have E3Live, use a blue-green algae or spirulina.

Contributed by:

Yasmin Gow (www.PracticeBliss.com)

Black Sesame Jewel

2 tablespoons black sesame tahini
5 semi-soft dates, pitted
1 cup water

Blend all ingredients until smooth.

Contributed by:

Ani Phyo (www.AniPhyo.com)

The BlueBerrian

1 ½ liters water
½ cup hulled sesame seeds
½ cup coconut flakes
1 tablespoon milk thistle seeds
15 apricot kernels *(more info on page 71)*
3 tonka beans
3 vanilla bean skins *(save the inner seeds for the next stage of the drink)*

½ cup chia seeds, soaked *(gel)*
1 cup blueberries, fresh or frozen
1 teaspoon maca powder
Inner seeds from 3 vanilla beans
Agave *(amount to desired sweetness)*
Small pinch whole sea salt
1 teaspoon lecithin *(optional)*

Blend the first group of ingredients together, then pour through a strainer or nut milk bag. Add back to clean blender. Next, add the rest of the ingredients. Blend thoroughly, but not until warm. This wonderful summer is cooling (high calcium and lysine) and blood thinning (coumarin from tonka beans), as well as strongly antioxidant. It also provides ample nutrition to fuel a days worth of activity!

Contributed by:

Daniel Vitalis (www.ElixirCraft.com)

WHAT ARE TONKA BEANS?

Tonka beans are known for their fragrance, which is reminiscent of vanilla, almonds, and cloves. Tonka beans, sometimes used as a vanilla substitute, contain coumarin, an anti-inflammatory and blood thinning agent. While they are said to lighten one's mood and be emotionally balancing, the beans should not be used in large doses.

WHAT IS MILK THISTLE?

Milk Thistle is a plant native to Europe whose active constituent is silymarin, a flavonoid found in the seeds. Silymarin has been shown to have a tremendous affect on the health of the liver, protecting it from damage and enhancing the detoxification process. It acts as an antioxidant, and in milk thistle, has often helped to treat cirrhosis of the liver, chronic hepatitis, and inflammation of the bile duct. Milk thistle extract is commonly found in health food stores.

Bombay Diner Drink

1 cup water
½ cup sprouted mung beans *(remove any unsprouted beans)*
1 teaspoon fresh ginger root, peeled and diced *(or ¼ teaspoon ginger powder)*
1 tablespoon virgin coconut oil, liquefied
1 tablespoon shelled hemp seeds
1 tablespoon sweetener of choice *(i.e., raw honey)*
½ teaspoon cinnamon powder
½ teaspoon cardamom powder
¼ teaspoon clove powder
¼ clove fresh garlic
1 pinch Himalayan pink salt
1 tiny pinch cayenne powder *(or a tiny piece of fresh pepper)*

Place all ingredients in a blender and blend until smooth. The mung beans may leave a chalk-like powder in the smoothie; this may be removed by straining the smoothie through a nut milk bag, paint strainer bag, or cheesecloth. To liquefy the coconut oil, put the required amount in a mason jar and then place the jar in warm/hot water.

Contributed by:

Craig Sommers (www.RawFoodsBible.com)

WHAT ARE MUNG BEANS, AND HOW DO YOU SPROUT THEM?

Mung beans are small beans that sprout easily. The sprouts are high in vitamin C. To sprout: Rinse beans, then soak in warm water for 8-12 hours. Drain, gently rinse, and then place beans loosely in a paper towel or nut milk bag. Place in a large bowl or pot. Store for 24 hours, covered in warm darkness. You may gently rinse and re-store for another day to grow them longer, if desired. In either case, some people gently rinse and drain every 10-12 hours.

ChagaCoolnilla

Chaga *(innonotus obliquous)* *(a piece the size of a tennis ball)*
⅓ cup fresh ginger, sliced
½ cup goji berries, roughly chopped
½ cup dried coconut flakes
1 vanilla bean skin *(save the inner pulp for later in the recipe)*
1 cup mixed seeds/nuts
1 tablespoon purple corn extract
2 Balinese long peppers
Vanilla *(the pulp from the inner bean that was in the tea)*
Raw honey *(amount to taste, about 4–6 tablespoons)*
1–2 cups chia seeds, soaked to a gel or desired consistency
Pinch whole sea salt
6 tablespoons cacao powder
2 tablespoons maca powder
3 tablespoons coconut butter
1 tablespoon lecithin *(optional)*

Decoct (boil) Chaga in 1.5 quarts of fresh spring water for ½ to 1 hour. Reduce heat and add the ginger, gojis, coconut, and vanilla bean skin. Allow to simmer until the smell becomes strongly fruity. Strain and allow to cool. Pour this into a high speed blender and add the seeds (I prefer hulled sesame, coconut flake, Brazil nuts, apricot kernels, and milk thistle). After blending, pour the mixture through a strainer. Then, pour the nut milk back into the blender and add the rest of the ingredients. Blend and taste. Allow room for minor taste preference adjustments. Chaga is one of the most noble medicinal mushrooms, growing throughout the temperate zones of the world. It is easily identified and wild harvested, as it is almost exclusively found hosted on birch trees. This recipe is a superior immune system modulator, antioxidant, and anti-inflammatory. It is rich in Omega-3 fats, protein, and beneficial water-soluble fibers.

Contributed by:

Daniel Vitalis (www.ElixirCraft.com)

China Express

1 cup water
¼ cup goji berries
1 teaspoon fo-ti *(ho shou wu)*
3 gingko nuts, shelled
1 tablespoon astragalus root powder
Raw honey *(amount to taste)*

Blend to desired consistency.

Contributed by:

Anthony Anderson
(www.RawModel.com)

WHAT IS ASTRAGALUS ROOT POWDER?

Astragalus is traditionally used for its immune-enhancing properties and is known as the 'chief energy tonic' of traditional Asian medicine. The herb is harvested for its roots and has been prescribed to help heal the respiratory system and stimulate the immune system, especially the spleen and blood.

Astragalus comes in the form of tea, powder, and as an extract. The powder is mildly sweet and is great for smoothies.

WHAT ARE GINGKO NUTS?

This sweet nut comes from the center of the inedible fruit of the maidenhair tree, native to China. They are usually available dried, and fresh in season, at some specialty and Asian markets. You can find these at www.Sunfood.com.

Delicious Chocolate Dream

2 bananas
1 avocado
¼ cup raw chocolate
¼ cup agave nectar
1 tablespoon coconut oil
2 tablespoons lucuma powder
2 teaspoons maca powder
½ teaspoon cinnamon
1 cup water

Are you looking for the best raw smoothie recipe? Then, I think you are at the right place—I can eat this smoothie every day! This smoothie is not only one of the best on Earth, it is also very healthy. It contains the raw superfoods chocolate, avocado, lucuma, maca and cinnamon. These foods are all very high in nutrients, which makes them so-called 'superfoods'. By eating superfoods, you get the most nutrients per calorie, which makes them the best foods to lose weight, to recover from disease, or to become your own superhero. Raw chocolate also helps to lower appetite, in case you tend to eat too much. Can you think of something better than eating raw chocolate? Your family and friends will hardly believe you when you tell them how healthful it is. Put all ingredients in your blender, blend, and serve in nice glasses.

Contributed by:

Annet van Dorsser (www.RawFoodSuccess.com)

Easy Liver Detoxifier

1 ½ liters water
½–1 cup dandelion root
1–2 tablespoons yellow dock root
1 tablespoon milk thistle seeds
¼ cup coconut cream *(butter, not oil)*
Pinch whole sea salt
Yacon syrup *(amount to desired sweetness)*
1–2 tablespoons ramon nut *(optional)*
1 tablespoon tocotrienols *(optional)*
1–2 cups water
1–4 tablespoons psyllium husks

This is a more scientifically sophisticated drink, designed to flush the liver without the challenges and restraints of a traditional liver/gallbladder flush. Decoct 1 ½ liters of water, the dandelion, and yellow dock for 20 minutes, allowing to cool. Blend in the milk thistle seeds, then pour through a strainer. Add back to blender with the coconut butter, salt, yacon syrup, and optional ingredients (if desired). Blend and drink while still warm. The action of the coconut fat, coupled with the dandelion and yellow dock root will quickly induce a comfortable bile secretion, which is usually noticeable. A half-hour later, mix the psyllium into the water and drink quickly and immediately (it will begin to gel). The resulting gel will act as a 'sponge,' mopping up bile, stones and toxins. This is easily eliminated as a bowel movement within a day.

Contributed by:

Daniel Vitalis (www.ElixirCraft.com)

Daniel Vitalis is a health motivator, strategist, and tonic elixir alchemist. The creator of ElixirCraft, he has been deeply immersed in raw foods, superfoods, herbalism and live food nutrition for more than 14 years. He draws from a vast reservoir of knowledge, ranging from physics and anatomy to alchemy and astrology. He leads workshops, tele/video conferences and classes, and retreats, as well as private consults, catering, and recipe/menu development.

Kevin Gianni Says...

DO YOU REALLY HAVE TO CHEW A SMOOTHIE?

Yep! Just because you are blending doesn't mean you get a break from chewing! Even though this meal is liquid, you still have to chew your smoothies—just like you were eating solid food. In fact, gulping the thing down is one of the biggest mistakes you can make. Doing so doesn't allow the enzymes in your saliva to begin breaking down the sugars in the drink. By slowing the start of the digestive process in your mouth, not only does the stomach have a harder time doing its job but more sugar will enter your blood stream. High blood glucose levels can cause long-term digestive disorders.

So, it's really important to chew your smoothies. I know it sounds weird. I know it looks weird. I know it feels weird. But it's something you will have to adhere to if you want optimal health!

Flying High Goji Berry Bonanza

4 cups liquid *(water, or hot or cold tea)*
Fresh coconut water *(or any nut milk)*
3 tablespoons cacao powder
1 tablespoon cacao nibs
1 tablespoon maca, red maca or maca extreme *(if you dare!)*
3 tablespoons certified organic goji berries
1–2 tablespoons sweetener of your choice *(i.e., raw honey)*
1–3 cups organic berries or fruit, frozen
1 tablespoon hemp seeds
1 small pinch Celtic sea salt
1 teaspoon goji berry extract powder *(optional, but super energizing)*

Try this awesome recipe to energize you any time of the day! Just blend everything together, adding berries until the desired consistency is achieved, and enjoy. Most of the ingredients above are available through Sunfood Nutrition. For the sweetener, I suggest any of Sunfood Nutrition's yacon syrup, amber or dark agave, or any of the raw honeys.

Contributed by:

David Wolfe (www.SunFood.com)

David Wolfe is the author of the bestselling books *Eating for Beauty*, *The Sunfood Diet Success System*, *Naked Chocolate*, and his newest release *Amazing Grace*. He is supported in his nutrition mission by Sunfood Nutrition™ (www.SunFood.com), the world's largest distributor of books, juicers, audio/DVDs, organic beauty products, bulk organic foods, and exotic raw foods to assist people in adopting, maintaining, and enjoying plant-food-based lifestyles.

Global Superfoods Smoothie

Handful almonds, soaked and peeled
Handful goji berries, soaked *(or lycium fruit)*
½ mango
1 tablespoon raw cacao
2 tablespoons agave nectar
½ tablespoon lucuma powder
¼ teaspoon maca powder
¼ teaspoon raw ho shou wu powder *(fo-ti powder)*
¼ teaspoon ginseng powder
½ cup water

This smoothie is made with ancient superfoods from opposite sides of the world. Goji berries, raw cacao, lucuma, and maca are from South America. Lycium fruit (the same as goji berries), ho shou wu, and ginseng are from China. The unique combination of these ingredients—the best from around the world—boosts energy, strengthens the immune system, and increases physical power and mental clarity. Soak the almonds for at least 4 hours, put them in hot water for a few minutes, then strain; they should then be easy to peel. Put everything in a blender and blend until smooth. Feel the superpower of nature!

Contributed by:

Annet van Dorsser (www.RawFoodSuccess.com)

WHAT IS GINSENG POWDER?

Long revered in Chinese medicine, Ginseng is a slow-growing plant in the genus Panax (you may have seen "Panax Ginseng" for sale in health stores), the roots of which are used for various purposes, ranging from serving as a general stimulant to treating various health conditions. It's available in many forms, including a powder. Note that "Siberian" ginseng is not actually true ginseng; look for Panax.

The Hive

2 tablespoons raw honey
¼ cup bee pollen
1 teaspoon royal jelly
1 avocado
1 cup water

Blend to desired consistency.

Contributed by:

Anthony Anderson (www.RawModel.com)

. . . .

Kevin's Special Lemon Squeeze

1 lemon
½ inch fresh ginger
1 mango
1 banana
1 tablespoon maca powder
1 tablespoon hemp seed
1 handful of cilantro
Coconut water or plain water

This is a great smoothie for hot days and after a workout. Throw everything together and blend, adding water until desired consistency is reached.

Contributed by:

Kevin Gianni (www.TheRenegadeHealthShow.com)

Horchata

1 ½ cups almond milk *(see instructions page 19)*
½ cup fresh coconut meat
6 tablespoons sweet brown rice
2 large dates
½ teaspoon cinnamon
Pinch Celtic sea salt
Dash nutmeg

This is my raw version of a well-known Mexican drink. I first tasted it in my step-father's Mexican restaurant and have always wanted to duplicate the flavor raw. To make it, first soak the sweet brown rice in filtered water for 24 hours at room temperature. Use a Mason jar and cover with a breathable cloth. (No need to change the water.) Rinse and drain the rice. Pound the rice as finely as you can in a granite mortar and pestle. Put all ingredients, except the nutmeg, into a blender and blend well. Serve in a tall glass and sprinkle with nutmeg. Note: If you double the recipe, do not double the amount of rice used, as 6 tablespoons of rice will flavor a double portion as well.

Contributed by:

Rhio (www.RawFoodInfo.com)

Illuminated Being Elixir

WHAT IS WHITE TEA?

White tea, which undergoes even less processing than green tea, is considered to be the healthiest of teas. The leaves are picked while they are still immature, before the buds are fully opened. Thus, this mild-flavored tea contains more polyphenol antioxidants than any other tea. Studies have shown that it enhances the immune system and contains natural fluoride, which helps reduce dental plaque.

WHAT IS AN ASIAN PEAR?

Asian pears are sometimes confused with pear-apple hybrids. However, they're simply a normal pear variety, known under many names: Japanese pear, Nashi pear, or apple-pear. The 'apple confusion' likely derives from this pear's shape and texture, both somewhat apple-like.

If you can't find an Asian pear, try substituting any other variety of pear.

¼ cup coconut milk
¾ cup white tea
½ cup apple juice
1 Asian pear
Handful bean sprouts
1 teaspoon rice bran
1 teaspoon raw honey

Blend everything together to make a crown chakra (Sahasrara) smoothie. The crown chakra is violet or white and rests at the top or just above our head. Said to be our gateway to the divine, it is connected to spirituality, wisdom, and knowledge. The special ingredients in this smoothie, like white tea and rice bran, are designed to provide for overall well being, pleasure, and ease. They also provide an amazing combination of flavors; drink and be illuminated!

Contributed by:

Yasmin Gow (www.PracticeBliss.com)

Liquid Chocolate by Shazzie

1 cup raw almonds, soaked for at least 4
   hours
2 ½ cups water
Pinch Himalayan pink salt
⅓ cup raw cacao butter, gently melted
¼ cup lucuma powder
⅛ teaspoon Etherium Gold
1 teaspoon purple corn extract
¼ cup raw cacao powder
⅓ cup agave nectar

The cacao gods have my full attention, as I love raw chocolate as much as life itself. Add all ingredients to a high-speed blender (liquids first, powders and nuts second), and blend until smooth.

Contributed by:

Shazzie (www.shazzie.com)

WHAT IS PURPLE CORN EXTRACT?

Purple Corn, a traditional Andean food, has been cultivated in South America for centuries. It has a high phenolic content, and is also loaded with antioxidants and anti-inflammatory compounds. Purple corn is also high in anthocyaninins, which encourage connective tissue regeneration. Essential Living Foods™ makes an Organic Purple Kculli Corn Extract powder. The extract is made my juicing the corn and slowly evaporating the liquid at low temperatures; thus, it is very potent!

You can replace purple corn extract with any antioxidant-rich extract, or you can just leave it out.

WHAT IS MARINE PHYTOPLANKTON?

From the Ethos website (www.MarinePhytoplankton.net):

"Ethos Marine Phytoplankton is a single-celled aquatic organism, or micro-algae, and unlike many people believe, it is not a plant, seaweed, fungus, or herb. Unlike any other food, Phytoplankton is being hailed as the new 'super food,' as it is 100% nutritionally useful and completely bio-available to the body—when you eat it, nothing whatsoever gets wasted.

Ethos marine phytoplankton contains over 65 nutritional properties, including all of the amino acids, essential fats, vitamins, key minerals and trace elements, rare anti-oxidants, phospholipids, electrolytes, nucleic acids, enzymes, and coenzymes. With a pH of 8-8.5, it works to balance the body's own pH."

Love Sea Dancer

½ cup avocado
2 cups water
Pinch Himalayan pink salt
¼ teaspoon marine phytoplankton
1 teaspoon raw hemp seed oil
½ teaspoon Crystal Manna™
⅓ cup lucuma powder
1 apple, cored
⅓ cup agave nectar

This recipe is a gift to my ever-free friend and cacao visionary, Love Sky Dancer, who introduced me to the world of marine phytoplankton. Put all ingredients into a high-speed blender and blend until smooth.

Contributed by:

Shazzie (www.shazzie.com)

Mental Tune–Up

½ cup apple juice
2 tablespoons raw tahini
1 tablespoon lecithin granules
2 tablespoons wheat germ
1 tablespoon brewer's yeast
½ cup water
1 milliliter *(about 1 dropper full)* ginkgo extract

"Good morning!" You'll be saying that all day if you make this your regular wake up brew. This drink has all the vital ingredients you need for alertness and concentration. Lecithin, wheat germ, and brewer's yeast are our finest plant sources of phosphatidylcholine and acetylcholine. Acetylcholine is the most abundant neurotransmitter in the brain. Sesame seeds (tahini is sesame seed paste) are one of our best food sources for coenzyme Q10, nicotinic acid, phosphorus, and thiamine, all of which play a role in protecting our neurons from the damage caused by free radicals. Remember: Herbs and nutrients are not drugs. They nourish your neurons in a way that enables higher, long-term functioning. Chemicals may fire your neurotransmitters for a quick jump start, but leave you burned out. Real enhancement takes time. Regular consumption of the good nutrients in this drink, and others, will accomplish your goals. When you want to think fast, think smart. Blend the first 3 ingredients for 15-30 seconds, then add the powders and water and blend again. Finally add ginkgo extract. You may empty the contents of a ginkgo capsule into the blender if the preferred extract is unavailable. This drink will still be powerful even if you do not have all the ingredients.

Contributed by:

Steve Meyerowitz (www.Sproutman.com)

WHAT IS GUAR GUM?

Guar gum, which is extracted from the guar bean, is a water-soluble fiber that is used for a variety of purposes. Commonly, it's used as a thickener, which does not need heat to thicken. As it has almost 8 times the water-thickening potency of cornstarch, only a small amount is needed. It is sold as a powder in most health food stores.

WHAT IS YACON NECTAR?

Raw yacon syrup is a sweetener similar to molasses. Pressed from the yacon root, yacon nectar is good for digestion and helps absorption of calcium and vitamins. The sugar in yacon is mainly fructooligosaccharide (FOS), a type of sugar that can't be absorbed by the body. Thus, FOS acts as a prebiotic, serving as food for the "friendly" bacteria in the colon.

You can replace this with agave nectar.

Mint Ice Cream Shake

1 whole avocado, seeded and peeled
1 heaping tablespoon protein powder
½ cup almond milk (see instructions page 19)
½ cup coconut milk
¼ cup raw cacao nibs
1 handful spearmint leaves
3 cups water
Your choice of sweetener:
¾ teaspoon stevia extract powder
3 tablespoon raw yacon or agave nectar
18 drops of SweetFruit™ drops
Optional:
Ice *(amount to desired consistency)*
½ teaspoon guar gum
1 banana
Handful raw cacao nibs
⅛ teaspoon lemon juice

To make this more like a shake, add ice and half a teaspoon of guar gum powder. You can also add one peeled banana to the mix if you want a little sweeter taste. Throw in some raw cacao nibs at the end for mint chocolate chip ice cream. Also, you may want to add ⅛ teaspoon lemon juice to preserve the fresh, green color. Blend everything together, including the optional ingredients if desired, and enjoy.

Contributed by:

Mike Adams (www.NaturalNews.com)

Mushroomania

½ cup raw macadamia nuts
2 cups Pau d'Arco tea, cooled
Pinch Himalayan pink salt
¼ teaspoon lion's mane mushroom
    powder
2 teaspoons lucuma powder
⅓ cup raw yacon nectar

This smoothie is great for those who need extra 'Doxtoring,' as the special ingredients get to you the areas in your body that need help quickly. To make the tea, add 2 small spoonfuls of Pau d'Arco bark to a teapot, pour on hot water, and steep until cold. Strain the tea from the bark, discarding the bark. Add all ingredients to a high-speed blender and blend until smooth.

Contributed by:

Shazzie (www.shazzie.com)

WHAT IS PAU D'ARCO TEA?

Pau d'Arco (or Lapacho) tea is a rainforest medicinal made from the inner bark of the South American Tabebuia tree. Pau d'Arco is considered to be analgesic, antioxidant, antiparasitic, antimicrobial, antifungal, antiviral, antibacterial, anti-inflammatory, and laxative, as well as to have anticancerous properties. You can buy it loose or bagged.

WHAT IS LION'S MANE MUSHROOM POWDER?

Lion's mane (or Hericium) mushrooms are commonly prescribed in traditional Chinese medicine for stomach ailments and prevention of cancer. They have also been shown to be effective as an immune enhancer. The powder can be used as a flavoring in raw food preparation.

You can use any mushroom extract or powder to make this smoothie.

Nature's Antioxidant Blast

¼ cup blueberries
¼ cup raspberries
¼ cup strawberries
¼ cup blackberries
¼ cup cherries, pitted
1 banana
1 tablespoon ground flaxseed
1 tablespoon shelled hemp seeds
1 tablespoon barley grass powder
1 teaspoon chlorella powder
1 tablespoon non-GMO lecithin granules
¼ teaspoon turmeric powder *(or a coin-sized slice of fresh turmeric)*
¼ teaspoon ginger powder *(or a coin size-sliced of fresh ginger)*
1 dash cinnamon
2–4 whole cloves *(or ¼ teaspoon clove powder)*
1–2 cups water
¼ teaspoon virgin coconut oil *(optional)*
1 dash cayenne powder or part of a fresh pepper *(optional)*

Place all ingredients in a blender and blend until smooth. Feel free to substitute frozen berries for all of the fresh berries listed.

Contributed by:

Craig Sommers (www.RawFoodsBible.com)

Kevin Gianni Says...

WHAT ARE SOME GUIDELINES TO FOLLOW IF YOU WANT TO MAKE UP YOUR OWN RECIPES?

In my opinion, there are two different ways to going about inventing your own smoothie recipes. You can follow my guideline, which is to "look around, see what's in the fridge and cupboards, and mix some stuff together." In other words, 'MacGyver it.' Or, you can follow a more conservative guideline, which is "less is better."

I prefer a mix of fruit and green. So, I'll add a little bit of both. I generally start with a mango or a banana. They are both solid base fruits; they can sweeten up flavors that aren't sweet, and they can mask the flavor of smoothie items that might be bitter or have a taste that you don't like. When I add my greens, I use those that aren't too heavy or bitter. Two of my favorites are spinach and bok choy because they don't taste offensive when you mix them together. If you put mango and kale together, you're going to taste the kale; but, if you put mango and spinach together, you really won't taste the greens. So, using lighter greens are really nice if you've got a picky palate.

In terms of what you should add—if you're going by my guidelines for making different elixirs, just experiment! One day I was putting together a smoothie, and I decided that I was going to start with some mango. I added some cilantro, which I love. (Cilantro is another good green to put into the mix.) I added a lemon, some spinach, and bok choy. I put in some coconut water as a test, and then I said to myself, "This isn't enough!" So, I dug around the refrigerator and found some ginger. I popped the ginger in there, and man, the ginger brought my concoction from great to amazing. So, I recommend that you just try different things. Don't be afraid. You might waste one batch, but you might also make something that you will put in your arsenal of recipes forever! And, if you do waste it and make something that is awful, choke it down as punishment so you're not as careless the next time!

Ode to the PEA Brain

½ cup shelled hemp seeds
2 cups water
Pinch Himalayan pink salt
¼ teaspoon Blue Manna *(or other blue–green algae)*
⅓ cup raw cacao powder
⅓ cup raw carob nectar

It's my mission to allow my right brain to bask in the full glorious beauty of just being. This smoothie helps. Blend all ingredients until smooth.

Contributed by:

Shazzie (www.Shazzie.com)

WHAT IS BLUE MANNA™?

Blue Manna capsules and Crystal Manna powder are brand names of blue-green algae from Ancient Sun™, harvested and fresh-dried from Upper Klamath Lake. According to the Ancient Sun website (www.ancientsuninc.com), Blue Manna contains significant concentrations of Phycocyanin and PEA, or Phenylethylamine (thus, the name of the smoothie). It helps to promote greater mental clarity, attention, memory, and focus; emotional and mental balance; and healthy joints and tissues. It was developed especially for those who wanted ultimate nutritional support for the brain and nervous system.

You can replace this with any blue-green algae supplement or spirulina.

Rocket Fuel

1 cup apple juice
2 tablespoons tahini
½ banana
1 tablespoon lecithin granules
1 milliliter *(about 1 dropper full)* gotu kola, ginkgo, or guarana

Blend the banana, juice, and tahini together. Add about 1 dropper full of your favorite energy herbal extract (gotu kola, guarana, or ginkgo) to make a drink that provides many energizing minerals.

Contributed by:

Steve Meyerowitz (www.Sproutman.com)

WHAT ARE GOTU KOLA, GINGKO, AND GUARANA?

Gotu kola is an herb native to Asia. It's widely consumed as a general tonic and is linked to improved brain functioning (e.g., mental clarity and ability). Gotu kola is available in most health food stores in various forms.

Ginkgo, formally known as Ginkgo biloba, is a deciduous tree native to China. The tree has distinctive, fan-shaped leaves, and produces edible seeds. The ginkgo supplements found in most health food stores are made as an extract from the leaves. Like gotu kola, it's known as a brain function tonic, increasing alpha-wave activity in the brain and the number of neuroreceptor sites.

Gaurana is a plant native to South America. It bears seeds naturally rich in caffeine (more potent, even, than coffee!) As such, it's widely used as a general stimulant and tonic in South America and is increasingly becoming available in North America. You may want to be careful and use gaurana in small doses if you're sensitive to caffeine.

Shazzie's Silky Chocolate

½ cup raw almond butter
2 cups water
Pinch Himalayan pink salt
½ teaspoon green superfood powder, any brand
¼ cup raw cacao
1 banana
⅓ cup raw agave nectar

Blend all ingredients until smooth. Do try making this at home, especially with a spouse or lover. Don't worry if it drips all over you! ;-)

Contributed by:

Shazzie (www.Shazzie.com)

Slippery Road

2 tablespoons flaxseed
1 apple, cored
½ papaya or banana
2 tablespoons rejuvelac *(or other liquid or powdered acidophilus)*
1–2 cups water

Put the dry flaxseeds in the blender and blend into a meal. Then, add 1 cup of water and blend thoroughly. Next, add the papaya or banana and the chopped apple. Rejuvelac is a home-made, non-dairy acidophilus. Alternatively, add store-bought liquid acidophilus or another probiotic powder. Acidophilus is available as a powder and in capsules. Be sure to make it part of your daily diet.

Contributed by:

Steve Meyerowitz (wwwSproutman.com)

WHAT IS REJUVELAC?

Rejuvelac is a general term for a fermented liquid that is made by fermenting sprouted grains in water for a few days. It's known to improve one's bowel flora and, in turn, digestion. Rejuvelac is rich in enzymes and contains several vitamins and a variety of proteins and carbohydrates, among other nutrients.

Many raw food web sites single out wheat berries as the preferred grain to use in the process. However, some sources note that the drink can be made with a wide variety of grains, including whole wheat, rye, quinoa, oats, barley, millet, buckwheat, and rice. In either case, the grains are discarded in the end; it's the leftover water you drink.

There are many sites on the web that give detailed instrutions on how to make the fermented beverage.

WHAT IS OKRA, AND CAN I EAT IT RAW?

Okra, known to the scientific world as *Abelmoschus esculentus*, is the name of a tall, widely grown tropical plant —as well as the name of the edible pod for which the plant is famous (commonly found in vegetable soups, for example). Many people are unaware that okra may be eaten raw and is actually quite tasty this way. (If it wasn't edible raw, we wouldn't include it here in this book!) Give it a try sometime. And, if you live in a warmer climate, try growing some for yourself!

The Smooth Mover Smoothie

1 cup aloe vera gel
1 cup raw okra
Various fruits and vegetables *(amount to taste)*
3 cups water
Your choice of sweetener:
¼ teaspoon stevia extract powder
1 tablespoon agave nectar
6 drops of SweetFruit™ drops

You can add whatever fruits and vegetables you want. This smoothie is great for people with sensitive digestive tracts (irritable bowel syndrome, celiac disease, etc.), but be aware: the aloe vera gel can have laxative qualities if over-consumed. Combine ingredients and blend until extremely smooth. It is very important that you blend this particular drink until it is very smooth so that the raw okra can be well minced before you ingest it. For sourcing the sweeteners, I like www.cvc4health.com for the stevia extract powder, www.DragonHerbs.com for the SweetFruit drops, and www.GoodCauseWellness.com for agave nectar.

Contributed by:

Mike Adams (www.NaturalNews.com)

South American Supreme

1 avocado
1 teaspoon Pau d'Arco
1 teaspoon cat's claw
1 tablespoon lucuma powder
¼ cup Inca berries
1 cup water

Blend all ingredients to desired consistency.

Contributed by:

Anthony Anderson
(www.RawModel.com)

WHAT IS CAT'S CLAW?

Cat's claw is a tropical vine from South America and Asia, referred to as the 'Sacred Herb of the Rain Forest.' The inner bark and root are available as capsules, tea, and extract. Current studies show it may have positive effects on the body's immune system. Other constituents of the herb contain anti-inflammatory, antioxidant, and anticancer properties.

WHAT ARE INCA BERRIES?

Physalis peruviana, or Incan Berry, is a nightshade related to the common ground cherry in the U.S. These berries can be eaten raw, dried, or plain, and can as well be added to recipes. They are high in antioxidants and have anti-inflammatory effects.

Up All Night

½ cup raw tahini
2 cups yerba maté tea, cooled
Pinch Himalayan pink salt
1 teaspoon raw maca powder
1 teaspoon raw mesquite powder
⅓ cup agave nectar

Ecstatic beings sometimes need to stay up way past their bedtime so they can pull in divine light from the infinite Universe and spread it around the Earth— or so they can party just a little bit more. (People like me don't like to miss anything.) To make the tea, add 2 teaspoons of yerba maté leaf to a teapot, pour on hot water, and steep until cold. Strain the tea from the bark. Add all ingredients to a high-speed blender and blend until smooth.

Contributed by:

Shazzie (www.Shazzie.com)

. . . .

WHAT IS MESQUITE POWDER?

Milled from the bean and pod of the desert mesquite tree, mesquite powder has a sweet, nutty, chocolate-like flavor and can be used in baking or as a seasoning. Not only does it have a high flavor value, but the powder is highly nutritious as well. It contains digestible protein, lysine, calcium, magnesium, potassium, iron, zinc, soluble fiber, and Omega-3 fatty acids. It is also helps to balance blood sugar.

You can find mesquite powder through various online retailers and in some health food stores.

Vanilla Lavender Bliss

¾ cup almond milk *(see instructions page 19)*
¾ cup apple juice
1–2 drops lavender essential oil *(or 1 teaspoon lavender flowers)*
1 soft pear
½ banana
5 ounces soft tofu
1 teaspoon vanilla bean *(or ⅓ teaspoon vanilla extract)*
1 teaspoon tahini
1 teaspoon agave nectar

Blend everything to make an exotic, creamy smoothie that provides lots of protein. The lavender also adds restful and soothing properties. If you want to this to be 100% raw, replace the tofu with a protein powder of your choice.

Contributed by:

Rhio (www.RawfoodInfo.com)

IS CONSUMING ESSENTIAL OILS SAFE?

There are three main ways to use essential oils, and perhaps the one least thought of or understood is by ingestion. Taking EOs internally can increase their potency, but this can be safe! When choosing an oil to use internally, make sure that it is certified as GRAS, or Generally Regarded as Safe, by the FDA. Also, make sure the quality of the oil you select is guaranteed; it should contain no synthetic additives and be 100% pure. Likewise, it should not be decolorized, recolored, or deterpenated. Of course, only use essential oils that you trust. Some of the best ones for internal use come from small production facilities that carefully and slowly produce their oils at low temperatures. Two brands that we recommend are Young Living™ and Simplers™.

OUR AWESOME CONTRIBUTORS
MEET THE ULTIMATE SMOOTHIE TEAM

Mike Adams

Mike Adams began his mission as the Health Ranger as a response to his own failing health. At the age of 30, he was diagnosed with type 2 diabetes, a disease brought on by poor diet and severe lack of exercise. As a high-powered software executive, extreme levels of stress and cholesterol, depression, and chronic back pain were common features of Mike's past. Searching for answers to his health woes, Mike dove into research; he devoured thousands of books on nutrition, pharmaceutical drugs, wellness programs—anything he could find. He has now made it his life mission to share the most remarkable discovery he made on his quest: The vast majority of all diseases can be easily prevented and even cured without drugs or surgery. You can find out more on www.NaturalNews.com.

Anthony Anderson

Motivated by the desire to lean up and lose weight for his modeling career, Anthony happened upon a book about raw foods and decided to try it for two weeks. Aside from seeing physical changes almost immediately, he also experienced profound bursts of energy, happiness, and mental clarity and was convinced through his own trial, errors, and further research that eating raw/live foods is the way one should eat and live. He continues to document his journey of transformation and living a raw foods lifestyle on his blog, www.RawModel.com Though he enjoys modeling (for such companies as Hugo Boss, Macy's, Acura, and Paul Mitchell), his true passion is spreading ideas and awareness about green, simple living, and the raw foods lifestyle. Anthony is also a regular contributor to the biggest raw site on the net, www.welikeitraw.com. You can read more at www. RawModel.com.

Sergei, Valya, and Victoria Boutenko

Sergei Boutenko, a raw foodist for 15 years, graduated from Southern Oregon University with a B.S. in Human Communication. He is the co-author of the books *Raw Family*, *Eating Without Heating*, and *Fresh*. Sergei holds numerous certificates from different culinary schools. He is a raw food chef who has taught classes all over the world and has co-produced an award-winning movie, *Interview With Sergei Boutenko*. Sergei is an avid hiker, biker, runner, and student of capoeira.

Valya, also a raw foodist for 15 years, graduated from Southern Oregon University with a Bachelor of Arts in Fine Art. Valya is a certified raw food chef who specializes in desserts. She is the co-author of the books *Raw Family*, *Eating Without Heating*, and *Fresh*, and is the co-producer of the award winning movie, *Interview With Sergei*. She has been researching ways to inspire children to eat healthier. She practices nonviolent communication and is a student of Byron Katie. Valya enjoys gardening, dancing, sewing, and painting.

Victoria Boutenko is the award-winning author of *Green For Life*, *Raw Family*, *12 Steps to Raw Foods* and several raw recipe books. She teaches classes on raw food all over the world. As a result of her teachings, many raw food communities have formed in numerous countries. She continues traveling—sharing her gourmet raw cuisine and inspiring story of change, faith, and determination.

You can find out more about The Raw Family, who lives in Ashland, OR, on www.RawFamily.com.

Brendan Brazier

Brendan Brazier is one of only a few professional athletes in the world whose diet is 100 percent plant-based. He's a professional Ironman triathlete, bestselling author of *The Thrive Diet*, and the creator of an award-winning line of whole food nutritional products called Vega™. He is also a two-time Canadian 50km Ultra Marathon Champion. In 2006 Brendan addressed the U.S. Congress, speaking about the social and economic benefits that could be achieved by improving personal health through better diet. In 2007, he then lobbyed against the Farm Bill. Brendan has been named one of the most 25 Fascinating Vegetarians by *VegNews* magazine. His sites are www.BrendanBrazier.com, www.ThriveDiet.com, and www.MyVega.com.

Tamera Campbell

Tamera Campbell is the owner of Klamath Algae Products dba Vision/E3Live. Her areas of expertise are as varied as her numerous interests. Her dedication to the betterment of life for all inspired her 15 years as a dance instructor, working with students ranging from the highly gifted to those with mental challenges. Tamera is a frequent lecturer on detoxification and the body's elimination systems. She is the formulator of some of the top-selling green formulas on the market today, and her formulations are used by many world-famous doctors and healing clinics. Vision produces the revolutionary E3Live™, the world's first and only fresh-frozen Aphanizomenon flos-aquae (AFA). Tamera has had the great fortune of working closely with many highly respected and well-known healers who are living examples of the long term benefits of the living foods lifestyle, including Dr. Brian Clement of Hippocrates Health Institute. You can find out more at www.E3Live.com.

Brenda Cobb

After recovering from breast and cervical cancer in 1999, Brenda Cobb founded the Living Foods Institute in Atlanta, Georgia, to share her amazing journey and to teach the amazing detoxification methods–using raw and living foods–that had worked for her. Since opening the Institute, Brenda has expanded her Healthy Lifestyle Course to help people heal on every level. To date she has written nine books, including *The Living Foods Lifestyle*™; has appeared live on several major networks; and has inspired hundreds of thousands of people to take back their power and claim the perfect health they were created to have. Contact Brenda at 800-844-9876 or Brenda@LivingFoodsInstitute.com, www.LivingFoodsInstitute.com.

Dorit

Dorit's love for life and all of the experiences of a severe illness that brought her close to the brink of dying propelled her into writing *Celebrating Our Raw Nature: A Guide for Transitioning to a Plant-Based, Living foods Diet*. In addition to numerous guest appearances on television shows, Dorit is presently working on a DVD series and is also a host on the recently launched radio talk show called 'Recipes for Life' on IamHealthyRadio.com. Adding variety to her work as an author and speaker, Dorit works as a Certified Living Foods Chef, teaches for the Chopra Centre, coaches lifeskills groups, and runs a 'Fitness in the Park' program. Dorit is also the creator of a Raw Lifestyle Network Group and the founder of Serenity Foods™, her packaged food line that is under the distributorship of Vegan Traders. In 2007, Dorit founded and organized the first Raw Lifestyle Film Festival, which was such a huge success! Check out www.SerenitySpaces.org, or call (310) 854-2078.

Kevin Gianni

Kevin Gianni is the host of "The Renegade Health Show," a fun and informative daily health show that is changing the perception of health across the world. His is a successful author, a passionate natural health and raw foods advocate, a top-notch independent media producer and interviewer, a motivational speaker, and a mission-driven business coach. He is the author of *High Raw: A Simple Approach to Health, Eating and Saving the Planet*, and the co-author of *The Busy Person's Fitness Solution*. He created HealthBookSummaries.com with business partner Mike Adams and created the widely viewed "Rawkathon" interview series with leading experts in the raw foods movement. Follow Kevin on www.TheRenegadeHealthShow. com.

Annmarie Gianni

Annmarie Gianni is the co-host of "The Renegade Health Show," where she does weekly segments on fitness and raw food recipe preparation. She is a certified athletic trainer, massage therapist and the co-author of *The Busy Person's Fitness Solution*.

She received her Sports Medicine degree from East Carolina University. While doing so, she had the privilege of working with top Division 1 college athletes (including David Garrard, QB for Jacksonville Jaguars). She is the Owner of Lifestyle Fitness: In Home Personal Training, which you can learn more about on www.YourLifestyleFitness.com.

Throughout 2009 Annmarie is traveling the country with her husband, soul mate and life and business partner, Kevin Gianni, exploring the culture of natural health in America. (Their cat, Jonny 5, is along for the ride, too!)

Yasmin Gow

Throughout her childhood in Quebec, Jasmin was exposed to environmental and human rights activism, a variety of spiritual and holistic practices, as well as dance and gymnastics. Then, at 14 Yasmin found yoga—a perfect balance between it all. She started teaching in 2001 and has since trained professional athletes, given workshops all over the world, and founded PRACTICE BLISS™. Her unique style of teaching blends the dynamic flow of Ashtanga yoga and dance with postural alignment. Yasmin is also the creator of yoga CDs *Yoga with Pilates* and *Core Strength Power Yoga*, and is the Mind-Body-Soul columnist for *Jet Set Montreal* and www.Femmeaucube.ca. More on www.PracticeBliss.com. Yasmin@PracticeBliss.com.

Dr. Doug Graham

Dr. Graham is the author of several books on raw food and health, including *The 80/10/10 Diet*, *The New High Energy Diet Recipe Guide*, *Grain Damage*, *Nutrition and Athletic Performance*, and the forthcoming *Prevention and Care of Athletic Injuries*. He has shared his strategies for success with audiences at more than 4,000 presentations worldwide.

Recognized as one of the fathers of the modern raw movement, Dr. Graham is the only lecturer to have attended and given keynote presentations at all of the major raw events in the world, from 1997 through 2005. You can find out more at www.foodnsport.com.

Steve Meyerowitz

After 20 years of disappointment with orthodox medicine, Steve became symptom-free through his use of diet, juices, and fasting. He was christened 'Sproutman' in the 1970s by *Vegetarian Times*, as he was always surrounded by gardens of mini-vegetables. In 1980, he founded the 'Sprout House,' a 'no-cooking' school in NYC. Steve is a health crusader and author of 10 books, including *Power Juices, Super Drinks* and *Wheatgrass: Nature's Finest Medicine*. His most recent book is *The Organic Food Guide: How to Shop Smarter and Eat Healthier*. He has been featured on various networks and in various publications. His sprouting inventions, such as the 'Hemp Sprout Bag' are sold nationwide. Learn more on www.SproutMan.com.

Matt Monarch

Matt Monarch has been a 100% raw vegan for nine years and enjoys extraordinarily good health, bountiful energy, clarity of mind, and a deepened connection to nature. He was particularly attracted to the fact that this lifestyle offered increased longevity and freedom from degenerative disease. Matt's interest led him to thoroughly research the many different ideologies in the raw movement. As a result, he created–along with Dr. Fred Bisci, PhD–TheRawFoodWorld.com, a resource center dedicated to sourcing and providing the best products available. Matt also created www.LivingNutritionals.com to reach out to those who are interested in nutrition but are not necessarily ready to go raw. He is the author of *Raw Spirit*, which has become one of the best-selling raw books available, and *Raw Success*, which he considers his 'Bible' for the raw food lifestyle. He also spreads this message of health to others through two other websites, www.RawVeganBooks.com and www.RawSpirit.org.

Craig Pepin-Donat

Craig Pepin-Donat is the 'Fit Advocate', an international fitness expert, author of *The Big Fat Health and Fitness Lie* and founder of www.FitAdvocate.com, www.IHFSOnline.com (The International Health and Fitness Symposium) and www.WorstFitnessEquipment.com. Starting as a nationally certified personal trainer and rising to the top of his profession, Craig led several high profile fitness organizations as president and also served as executive V.P. of sales and marketing for the world's largest fitness organization. He has created numerous professional training programs, seminars and workshops, based on his simple formula for success that have helped millions of people get on the path to living a healthier and more active lifestyle.

Michael Johnigean

Michael Johnigean is a Florida native. He developed his first real estate company, MJ Investments, at the young age of 20. Over the next 18 years, he bought, sold, and developed over 2,000 properties while employing nine crews to renovate his homes. At the age of 38, he started Empire Development Group, which is responsible for starting several successful multi-million dollar projects throughout Florida. Always on the go, he knows how hard it is to find a quick and nutritious meal. Michael believes that nutrition is the key to a healthy life; it is our body's fuel source. Likewise, he says that the foods that we consume affect everything–how we think, look, and feel. Thus, he is currently developing the first of its kind: the all-natural and organic fast food restaurant, HealthyWay Café. You can find out more when you visit www.HealthyWayCafe.com. Michael has teamed together with Craig Pepin-Donat to reveal their favorite fruit smoothies.

Ani Phyo

Ani Phyo is the author of internationally acclaimed *Ani's Raw Food Kitchen: Easy, Delectable, Living Food Recipes*, which was awarded "Best Vegetarian Cookbook 2007." Ani's the host of the award-winning, number one 'uncooking' show on YouTube. She's been inspiring audiences with her fast, easy, delicious, healthy recipes and green lifestyle. Ani's shows can be viewed on her website www.AniPhyo.com.

Rhio

Rhio is a singer, author, and investigative reporter in the area of health and environmental issues. She is considered an expert in the area of raw and living foods. Rhio is of Hungarian-Cuban descent, raised in the U.S., but completely fluent in Spanish. Her first book, *Hooked on Raw*, is about living a life more closely aligned with nature by adopting a raw/live food lifestyle. The 358-page book also covers many of the reasons for making these healthy lifestyle changes and includes more than 350 raw, gourmet recipes. Currently, she is completing her third and fourth CD albums, one of which will tackle environmental issues and include some humorous raw food songs. A 3-DVD set of videos on raw food preparation entitled *What's Not Cookin' in Rhio's Kitchen* is set for release soon. Rhio hosts an internet radio show called *Hooked on Raw* ,which can be heard worldwide on two sites: www.TribecaRadio.net and also on www.HealthInfoRadio.com. Her website, www.RawFoodInfo.com, also provides extensive information on the raw/live food lifestyle, as well as on organic agriculture, environmental, human rights, civil rights, globalization and economic justice issues. Rhio and her partner Leigh are also fledgling permaculture, biodynamic, eco-farmers in Upstate New York.

Nomi Shannon

"A holistic physician introduced me to raw food in 1987 because I had serious digestive problems and felt ill no matter what I ate. I was gaining weight and had begun to develop an alphabet of maladies. With my physician's encouragement, I began to eat about fifty percent of my food raw. I began to feel better almost immediately. Soon after that, I embraced a 100% raw food diet. Over a matter of weeks, I said good riddance to fibromyalgia, hypoglycemia, mood swings, allergic sinusitis, and digestive disorders. It would be a lie to say that, in my mid-forties, I felt like I was in my twenties again; I had never felt as good in my twenties!" Find out more about Nomi Shannon and her book, *The Raw Gourmet*, on www.RawGourmet.com.

Shazzie

Shazzie, born in Yorkshire, England, became a raw foodist for health reasons at the age of 30. For almost four years (until she was overtaken by hormones during pregnancy), she ate an exclusively raw vegan diet. She now loves a 98% raw vegan diet. Becoming a raw foodist was an intrinsic part of her journey towards mental, spiritual, and physical freedom. She has been documenting her changes in her journal, which has been running for almost seven years now. Because of her open, honest, and personable writings, Shazzie attracts around 10,000 visitors to her web site every day. She founded detoxyourworld.com, which retails over 700 genuine health products. In addition, Shazzie has written five books, including *Detox Your World* and *Naked Chocolate*, co-authored with raw food guru David Wolfe. Shazzie has appeared in the media on numerous occasions and is a committed full-time mother. To find out more, or to book her for an event, visit www.Shazzie.com.

Dr. Craig Sommers

"Before starting on the path to conscious living and a mostly raw diet, I considered myself 'healthy.' True, I suffered from what I considered minor symptoms, including dandruff, athlete's foot, a small beer belly, as well as more serious conditions such as slow-moving bowels, poor memory, a short temper, and a chronic stuffy nose. When I cut out processed foods and animal products and started eating mostly raw foods, most of my symptoms vanished! My life improved markedly in many ways, as did my energy and attitude! In just five years, I went from working for others and just getting by to owning a health food store and earning a license in nutrition. Helping people stay healthy, or teaching them how to regain their health, is my life's work; I enjoy it very much!" Learn more at www.RawFoodsBible.com.

Angela Stokes

Award-winning raw food author, Angela Stokes, has an incredible story of recovery to share. Back in 2002, Angela, from Brighton, England, was 23 years old, weighed 294 lbs. and was depressed, lonely, and constantly ill. Then, in May 2002, she went 100% raw-vegan. She has since lost over 150 lbs. and has completely transformed her life. In January 2004, she set up her popular testimonial website, www. RawReform.com, to share her message of hope with others. The response has been incredible, and others have been inspired by her story to lose weight and reclaim their own health naturally. Her work attracts widespread recognition, including an award from the House of Lords in the UK and a national grant to support her website. She sells books on raw weight loss, gives lectures, holds retreats, and offers private consultations too. She can be contacted at Angela@ RawReform.com.

Annet van Dorsser

Annet van Dorsser is the founder of the popular blog, www.RawFoodSuccess.com, which is a great resource for everybody interested in natural health and the raw food diet. Annet also started the first raw food blog in Dutch (www.RauweVoeding.nl) and is the co-founder of Raw Food Europe and Raw Food Netherlands. Annet has studied almost all diets, major religions, and spiritual practices, including macrobiotics with Michio Kushi, the raw food diet with Ann Wigmore at the Hippocrates Institute, and child psychology and psychiatry at the University of Utrecht. Annet has also studied Chinese herbology and dietary therapy, and Ayurveda. She is one of the ten certified pediatric acupuncturists in the Netherlands. Annet is now a speaker, author, and health coach, working with people from all over the world.

Daniel Vitalis

Daniel Vitalis is a health motivator, strategist, and tonic elixir alchemist. The creator of ElixirCraft™, he has been deeply immersed in raw foods, superfoods, herbalism and live food nutrition for more than fourteen years. He draws from a vast reservoir of knowledge, ranging from physics and anatomy to alchemy and astrology. His method, which he calls 'ElixirCraft,' is the first codified synthesis of ancient and modern herbal/medicinal/nutritional drink preparation techniques. This liquid nutrition system is founded on the use of highest quality/potency, fresh-gathered spring water, which is the most abundant and important nutrient in the human organism. He leads workshops, tele/video conferences and classes, and retreats. He also does private consulting, catering, and recipe/menu development. For more information, visit Daniel at www.ElixirCraft.com, or contact Formulate@ElixirCraft.com.

David Wolfe

David Wolfe, health, eco, nutrition, and natural beauty expert, is the CEO and founder of Sunfood Nutrition (www.Sunfood.com), the president of The Fruit Tree Planting Foundation (www.ftpf.org), and the co-founder of TheBestDayEver.com. With a masters degree in nutrition and a background in science and mechanical engineering, David Wolfe is considered one of the world's top authorities on natural health, beauty nutrition, herbalism, chocolate, and organic superfoods. He has over 14 years of dedicated experience and understanding of the delicate chemistry and hardcore mechanics of the human body. He is the author of the best-selling books *Eating for Beauty*, *The Sunfood Diet Success System*, *Naked Chocolate*, *21-Day Peak-Performance Weight Loss Program*, and his newest release, *Amazing Grace*.

The Sun Warrior™ Team

Nick Stern

For most of his life, Nick Stern has shared a unique and passionate commitment to health, nutrition and fitness. At the young age of 13, he discovered the benefits of juicing, sprouting, fasting, and a raw-vegetarian diet. His quest for ultimate health has included a multitude of diet philosophies, ranging from a fruitarian diet to a high protein-low carbohydrate diet to a strict vegetarian, to virtually every other diet known to man. Most recently he is a self-professed 'superfoodtarian,' consuming foods primarily consisting of raw superfoods. At 55 years of age, he admits to feeling and being in the best shape of his life, and he is confident that through proper nutrition anyone can continue to look and feel vibrant at any age. To bring everything full-circle, he co-founded Sun Warrior, the leader in super raw vegan protein. His ultimate goal is to raise consciousness through raw superfoods and cutting edge supplements.

Brent Hauver

While working as a high powered sales and marketing manager in the Midwest for a large software company (WordPerfect Corp), Brent started having glitches in his health at the age of 23. The high stress, poor diet and on-the-go pressures caused him to experience fatigue, obesity, and low energy levels. In an effort to get his health to a premium, Brent started hanging out in health food stores and reading books from Paul Bragg, Arnold Ehret, and other health gurus. He became a vegan and eventually moved toward a raw food diet.

Initially he got better, but after 16 years on a raw-vegan diet, his health seamed to deteriorate. He lost weight and got extremely thin. He was becoming angry all of the time. His ability to digest food kept diminishing until he was wasting away to nothing. Finally, when his weight got down below 145 lbs (at 6'4"), he decided enough was enough; so, he started searching for a solution. He concluded that his diet of low, raw protein and high carbohydrates and low fat was killing his body and throwing its bio-chemical system out of balance. By using Sun Warrior Superfood protein as a base, he started doing a Sun Warrior Live Zone diet. It was not long until he totally transformed his health and fitness. He gained 45 lbs of muscle, and his energy levels and stamina went through the roof. To hear his story, you can listen to an interview with Mike Adams at (http://www.naturalnews.com/023282.html). The Audio link to the pod cast is interview #36 at (http://www.naturalnews.com/Index-Podcasts.html).

Denley Fowlke

Denley is a very successful and high-powered real-estate broker and developer in St. George, Utah. His quest for the highest possible health has led him to a vegan diet (over 15 years) and raw food (over 10 years). His combination of savvy business personality, mingled with his earthy environmental consciousness is a rare find. He is totally committed to creating an earth friendly solution for the earth and its environment.

RECIPES INDEXES

BY SUBJECT, SMOOTHIE, CONTRIBUTOR

Subject Index

NOTE: ADDITIONAL INFORMATION ON AND DEFINITIONS OF
CERTAIN ENTRIES CAN BE FOUND ON PAGES DENOTED BY AN *.

V

W

Y

Z

Smoothie Index

Fruit Smoothies

FRUIT SMOOTHIES CONT...

Green Smoothies

GREEN SMOOTHIES CONT...

Elixirs

ELIXIRS CONT...

‹

Contributor Index

Victoria Boutenko

Yasmin Gow

A Simple Approach to Health, Eating, and Saving the Planet

KEVIN GIANNI'S

High Raw

Kevin Gianni, internationally known health advocate, author, and producer of the hit internet TV blog, The Renegade Health Show, debunks a common myth about health—He teaches that it DOESN'T have to be hard!

Enter a New, Simple Paradigm of Health

With five easy principles, *High Raw* clears the confusion about nutrition science and gently encourages you to effortlessly create a lifestyle of sustainable health.
Are you ready to enjoy your health journey every step of the way? Are you ready to feel your best now AND in the future? Are you ready to feel more connected in mind and body to your community, and to the planet? If the answer is 'yes,' then get ready, get set, go! The time is now.

Start Your High Raw Journey Today!